TANGRAM PATTERNS

All drawings and many original
puzzles in this book were done by
THOMAS E. FOSTER

Creative Publications, Inc.

Limited Reproduction Permission: The author and publisher hereby grant permission to the teacher who purchases this book or the teacher for whom the book is purchased, to reproduce any part of this book for use with his or her students. Any further duplication is prohibited.

3.078.11   ISBN: 0-88488-081-8

Introduction

The tangram puzzle consists of seven pieces—five triangles, a square, and a parallelogram. These seven pieces can be cut from a single square. (See page 159 for a pattern to make your own set of tangram pieces.) Reassembling the seven pieces into various forms—birds, animals, etc.—provides hours of challenging fun.

The tangram puzzle originated in China. Many books of tangram puzzles were published in China in the early nineteenth century. Several of these books indicate that the origin of the puzzle was then unknown. This would indicate that the tangram puzzle is extremely old. Travelers brought the tangram puzzle to Europe and the United States in the nineteenth century. Books on tangrams were published in English. These were of generally poor quality and were mostly copies of the Chinese books of the period. Sam Loyd published a book in 1903 called *The 8th Book of Tan.* In Loyd's typical fashion, he spins tall tales about the history, scientific, and mathematical significance of tangrams. Others have joined Loyd in mystical ramblings about the origin and significance of tangrams.

Educationally tangrams provide a relatively simple, interesting problem solving situation applicable to all age groups. Discovery lessons and discussions of size, shape, congruence, similarity, symmetry, area, properties of polygons, etc. can be started or stimulated by exercises employing tangrams.

This book is divided into four sections. The first section shows tangram patterns outlining every piece. A student is merely required to place the seven tangram pieces on the puzzle page. The second section provides an outline of the figure to be covered, but does not indicate the exact placement of each piece. In addition, these puzzles do not use all seven of the tangram pieces. This feature of using fewer than seven pieces provides a transition to the third section where all seven pieces are used. Only an outline of the pattern is provided. The fourth section contains outlines which have been reduced and puzzles using two sets of tangram pieces.

Within each section an attempt has been made to arrange the puzzles in order of increasing difficulty. Strict order of difficulty is impossible to achieve. Some "bright" individuals may have a great deal of trouble with "simple" puzzles, while less able students may have no trouble solving the most difficult tangram patterns. This provides an opportunity for all students to participate with a high probability of success and enjoyment.

The purpose of this book is to provide a collection of tangram patterns which may be reproduced and used in the classroom. Possible approaches to take include:

1. Activity cards for math lab settings. Mount the pages on tag board and laminate or cover with clear contact. An alternative approach would be to insert puzzle pages in a 9" x 12" plastic activity card protector. Use these activity cards at math lab stations for problem solving challenges or as fun, reward activities for students who complete regular assignments early.

2. Copies for each student. Reproduce enough copies for each student by xerography or by making pages from a thermofax spirit duplicating master. Copies may be given to individual students or to an entire class as a problem solving activity. Discussion of 'discovered' geometric properties could lead to further learning.

3. Problem solving and creativity. Give copies of the tangram patterns to each student. After students have had time to become familiar with the patterns have them create new tangram patterns of their own. This could be approached as a problem solving activity by specifying the animal or design to be produced or as a creativity activity by allowing students unlimited freedom to create their own patterns. Patterns created by a student could be reproduced and given to other students. This may serve to increase interest and reward creativity.

Other related Creative Publications' products:

Tangramath by Dale Seymour

Tangrams

Tangram Stickers

Tangram Tracers

Tangrams by R. C. Reed

CONTENTS

TYPE I

Tangram Patterns

Tangram patterns with every piece outlined.

Contents

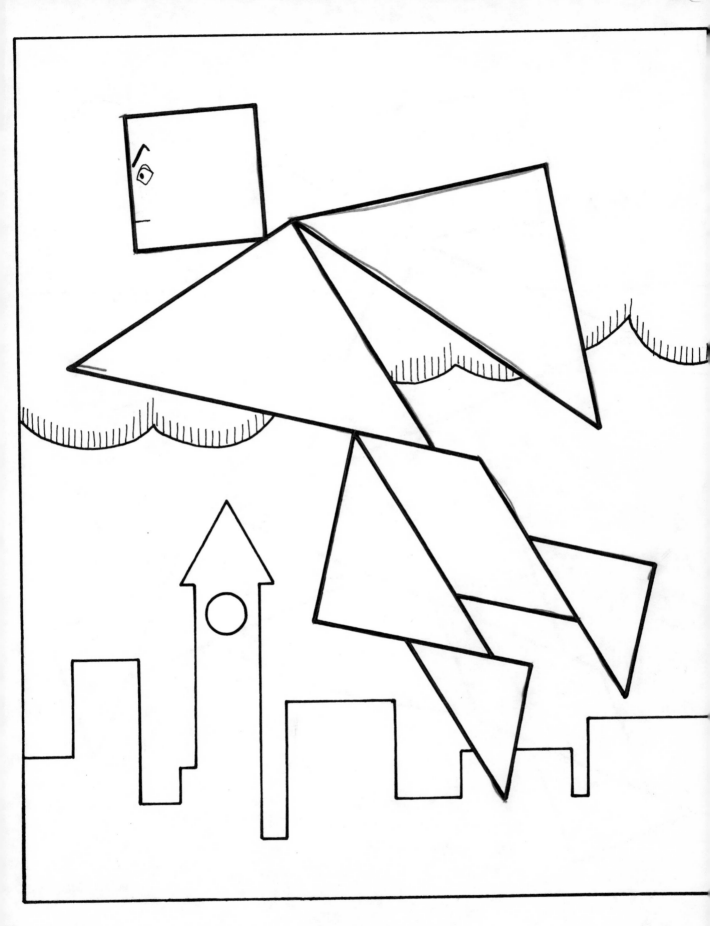

1　Superman flying

2 Running boy

3   Fred Flintstone

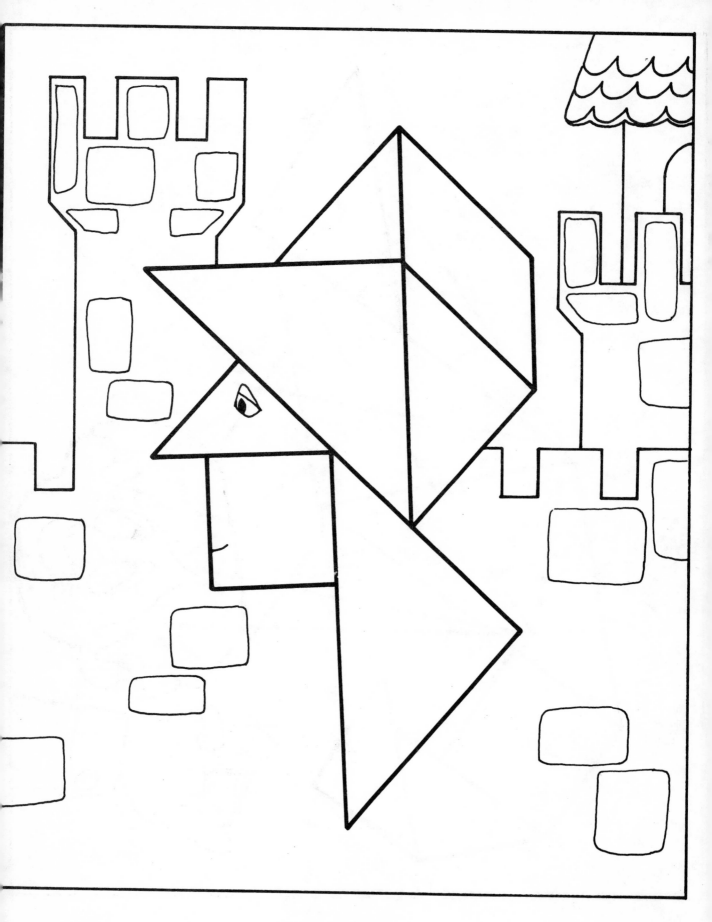

4   Soldier cap

5 Parrot

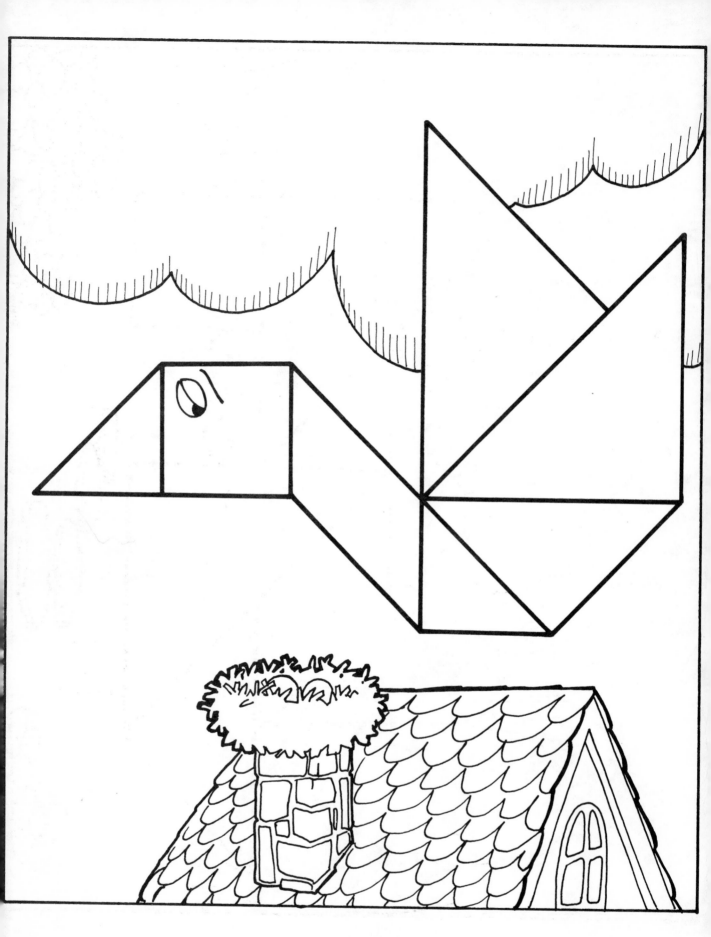

6   Stork

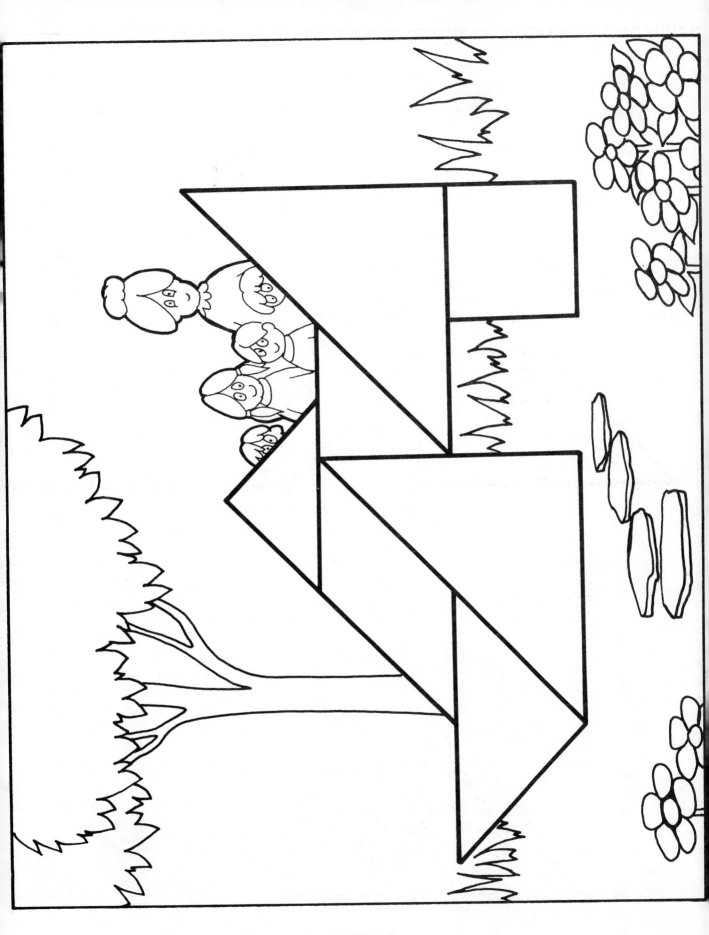

7　Shoe

8 Nail

9   Hexagon

10   Letter R

TYPE II

Tangram Patterns

Tangram pattern outlines using fewer than seven pieces.

Contents

11 Butterfly

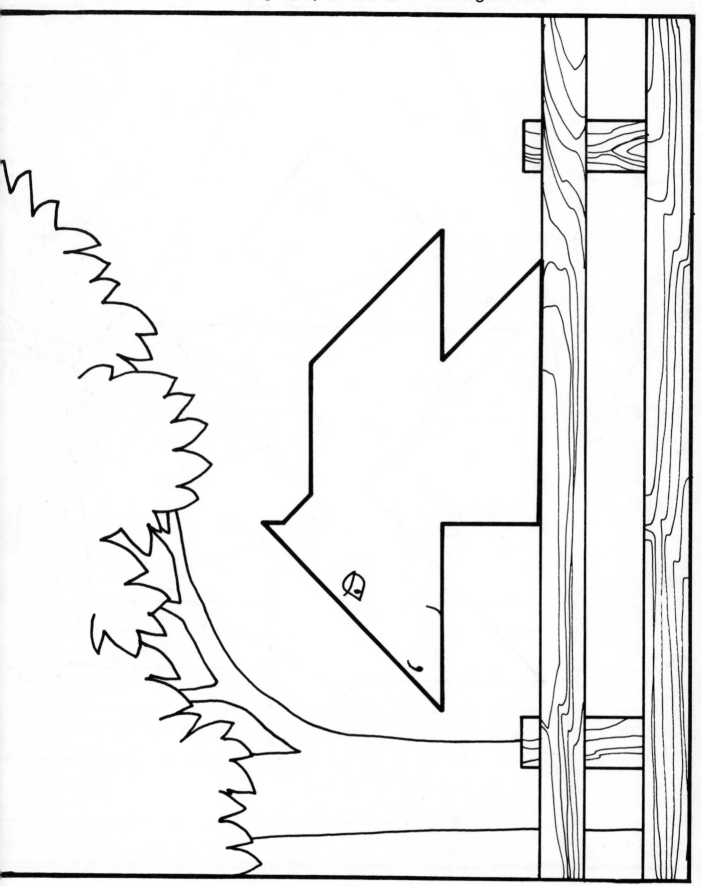

12 Horse's mane

With 4 tangram pieces make this figure.

13 Dancer

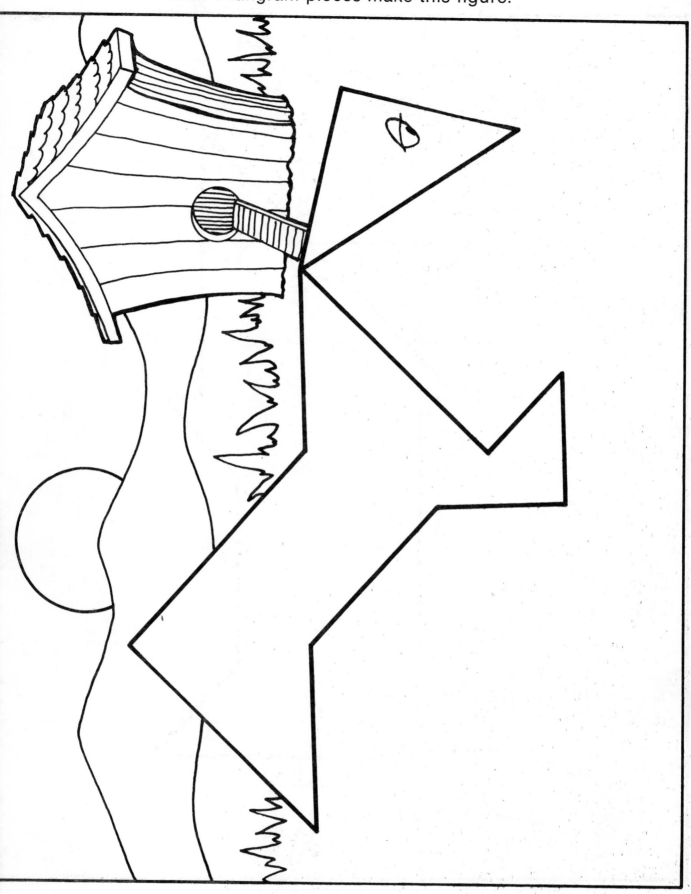

14 Chicken

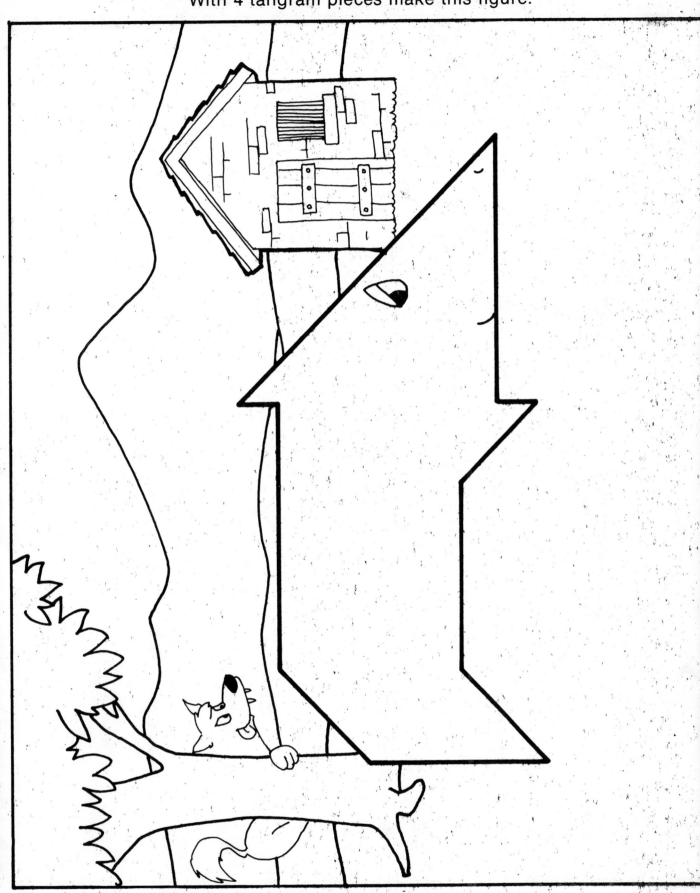

15 Pig

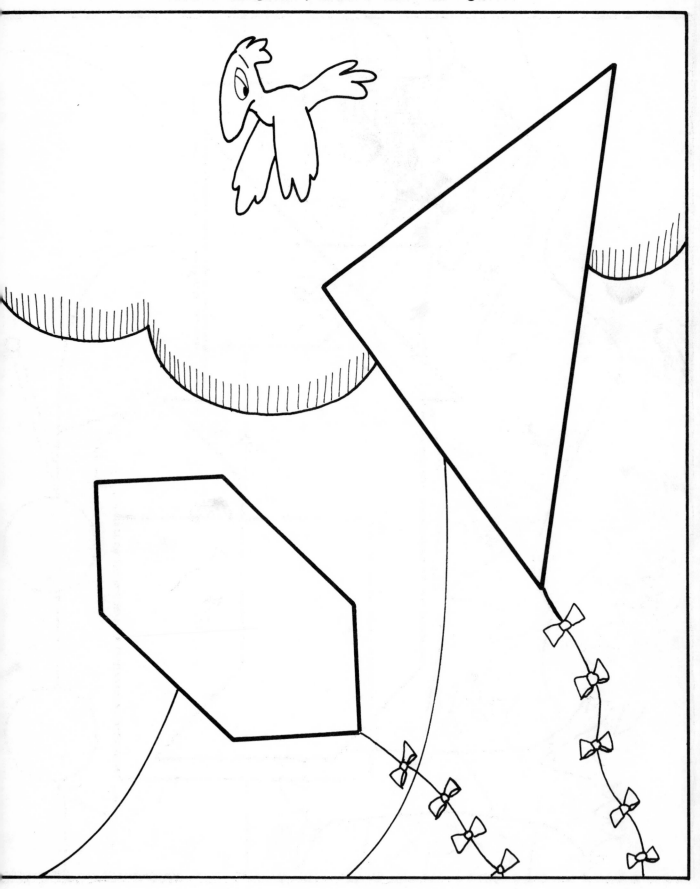

17 Hexagon
With 4 tangram pieces make this figure.

24

With 4 tangram pieces make this figure.

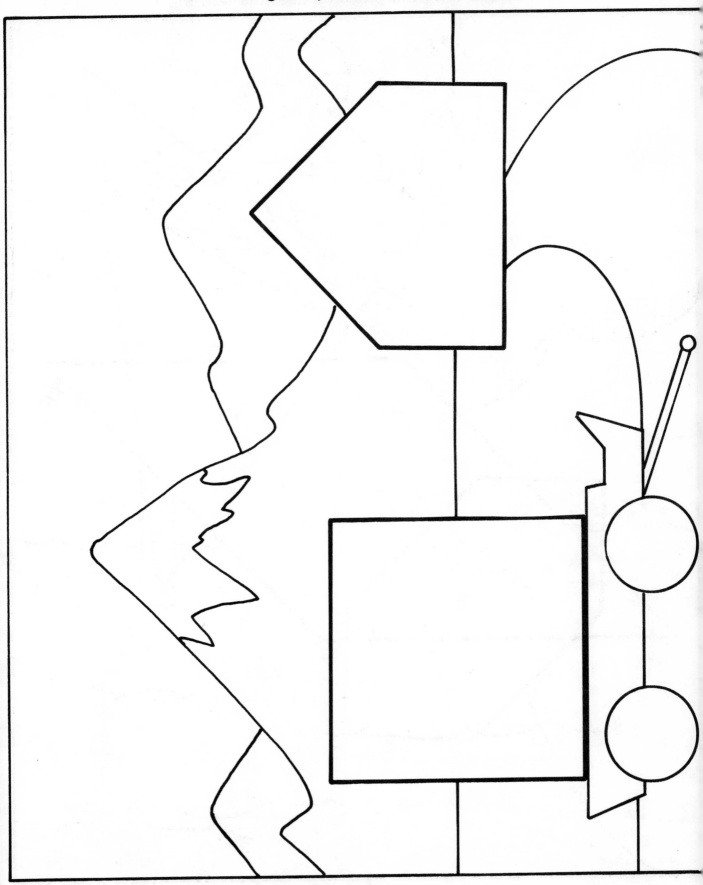

19   Square
With 5 tangram pieces make this figure.

20 Parallelogram

With 5 tangram pieces make this figure.

21 Isosceles trapezoid

22 Girl

23 Llama

24 Cat

With 5 tangram pieces make this figure.

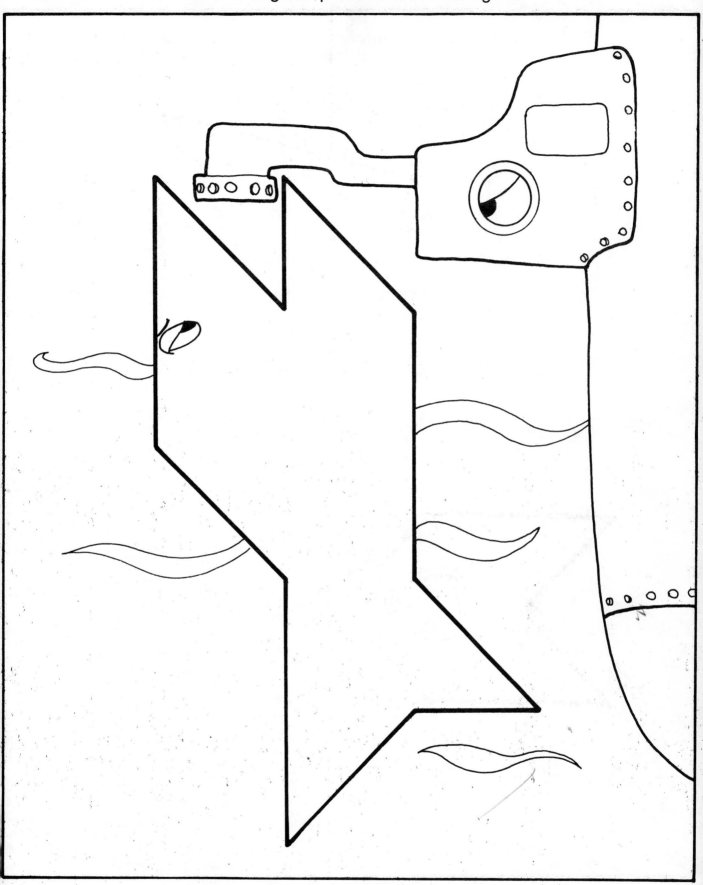

25 Shark

26 Owl

27   Barn and silo

TYPE III

Tangram Patterns

Tangram pattern outlines using
seven pieces.

Contents

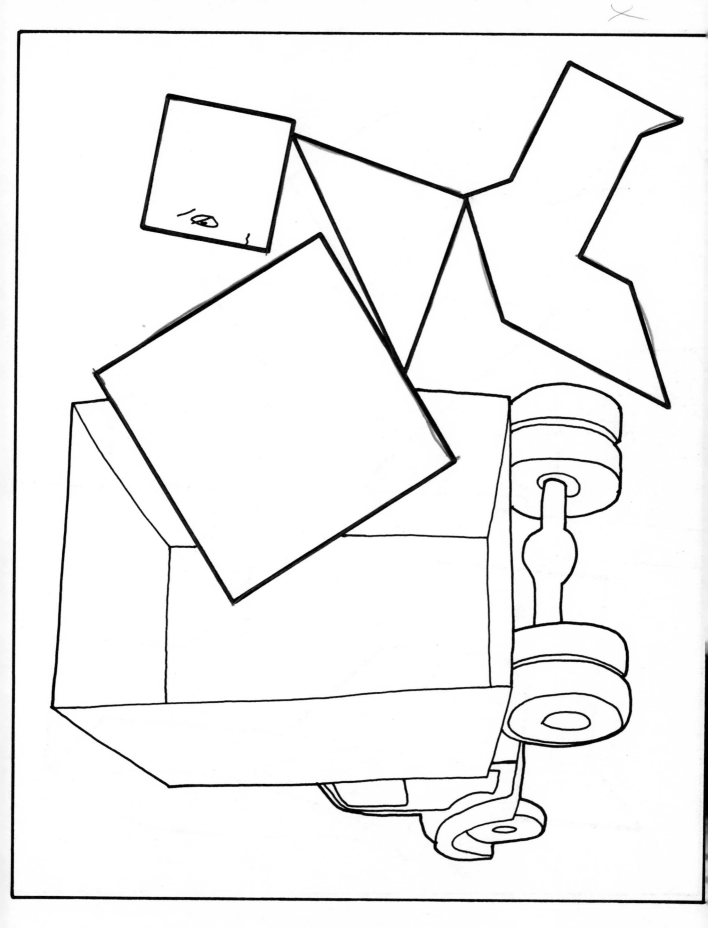

28 Mover

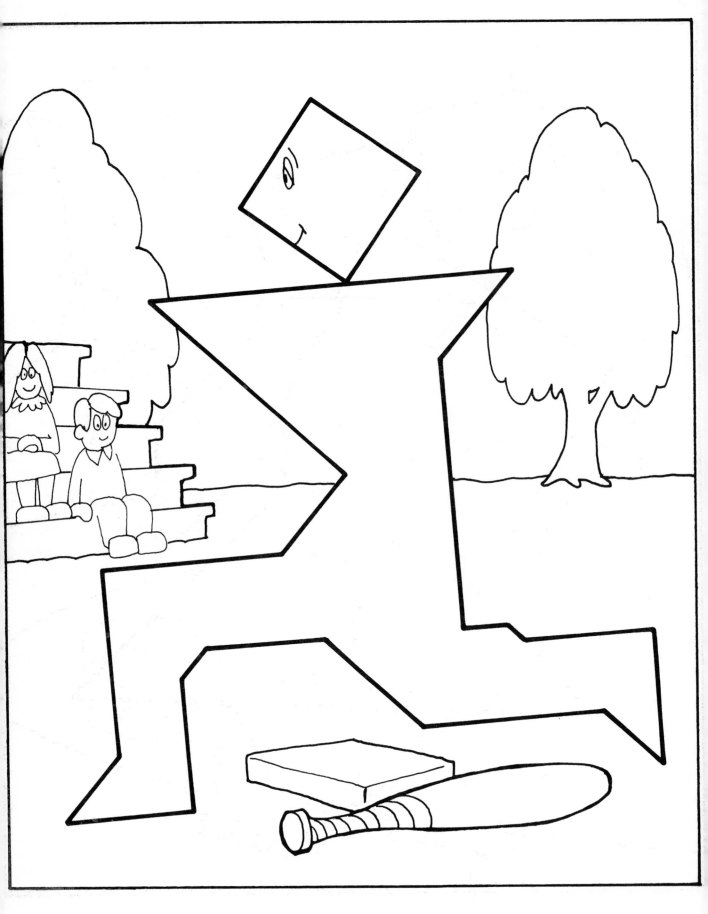

29 Boy

30 Walking girl

31 Running man

32 Cow

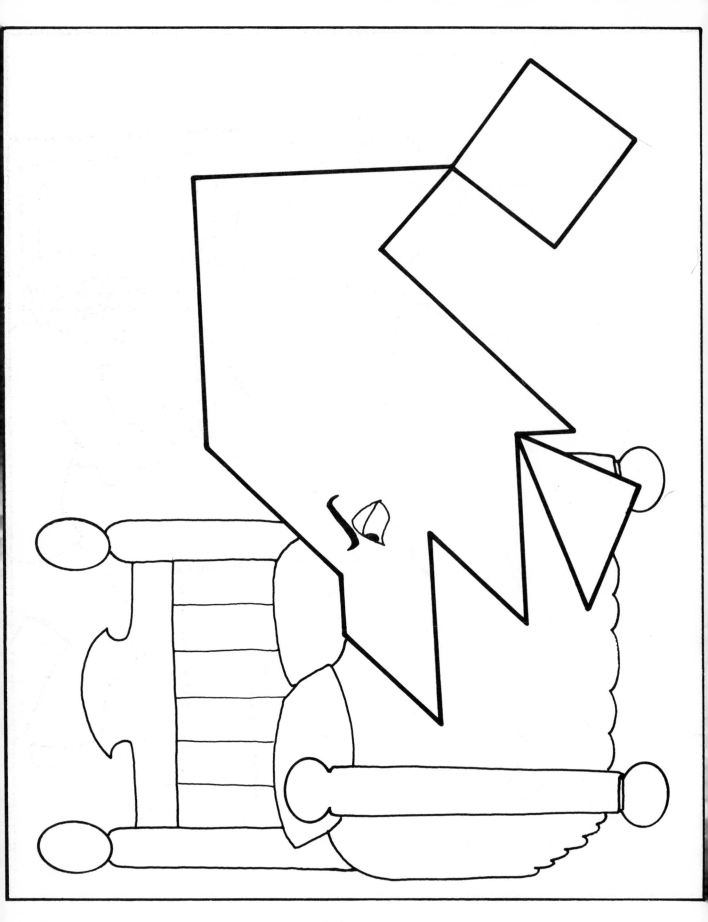

33 Scrooge

34 Super hero

35 Scuba diver

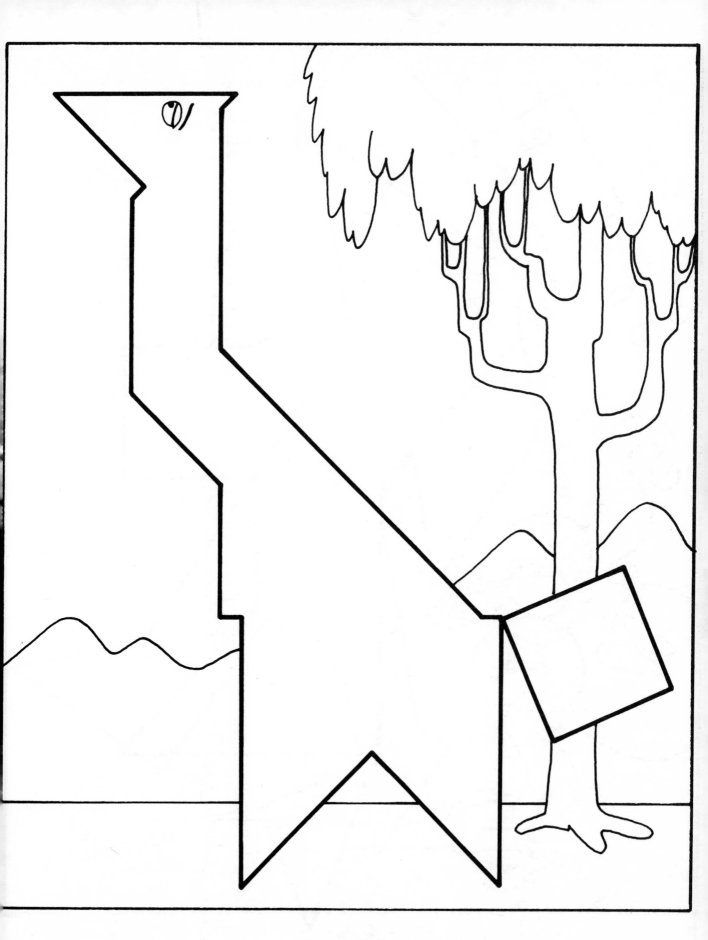

36 Giraffe

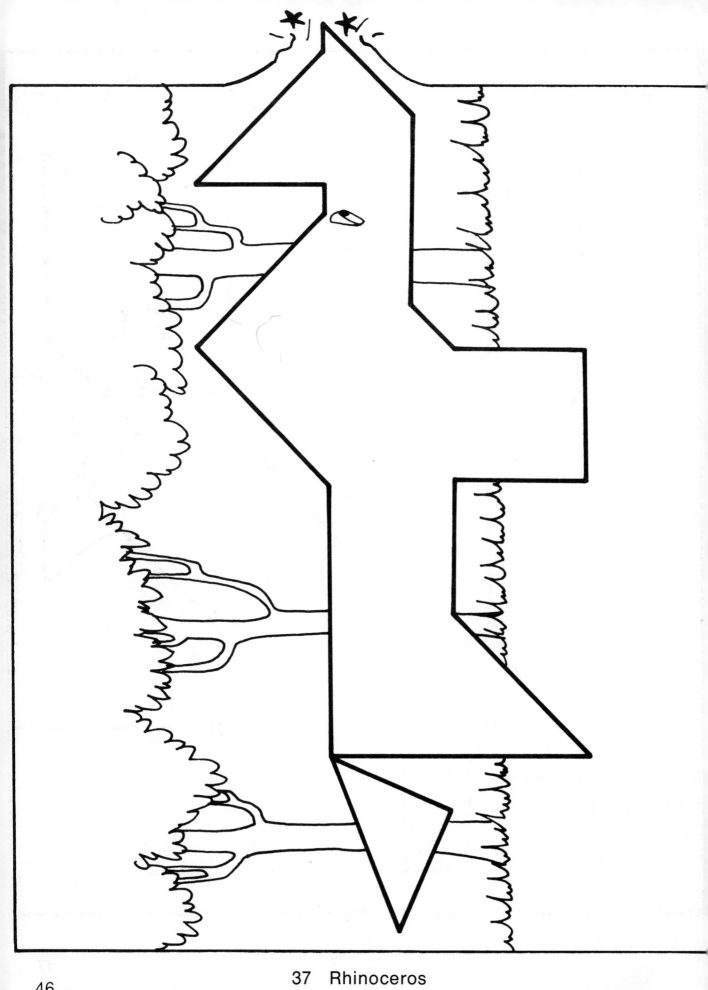

37   Rhinoceros

38   Sitting cat

39 Horse and rider

40 Swan

42   Letter A

43 Sitting Indian

44 Horse

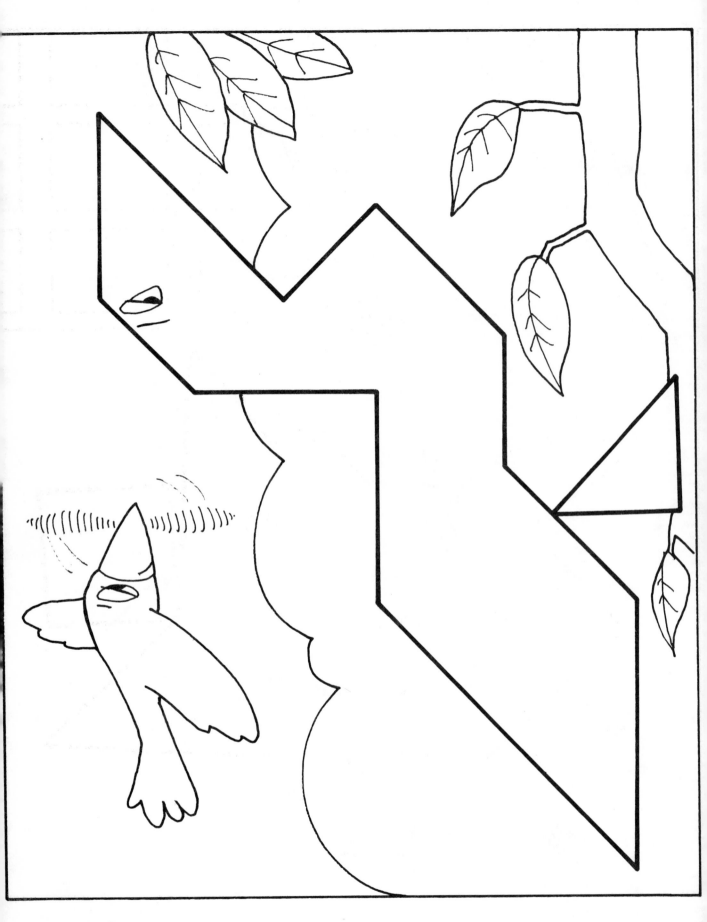

45　Bird

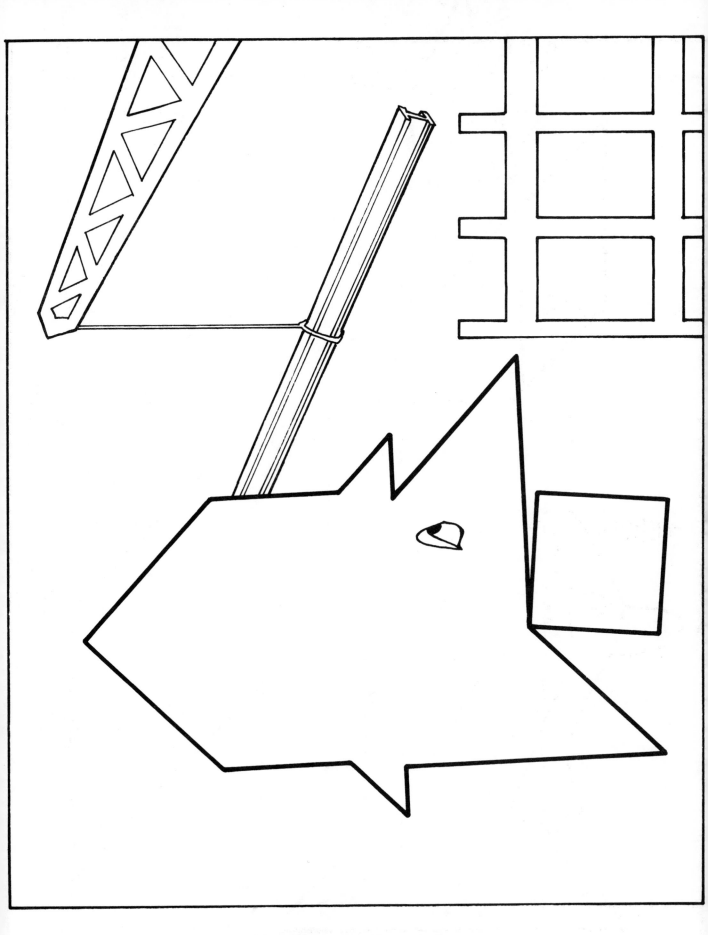

46 Construction worker

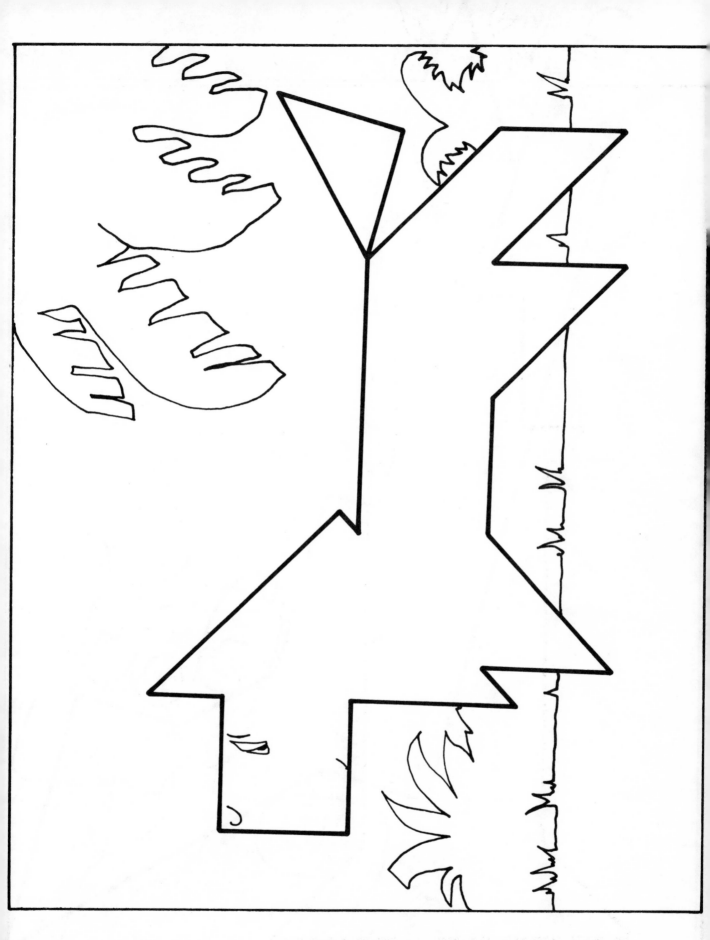

48   Lion

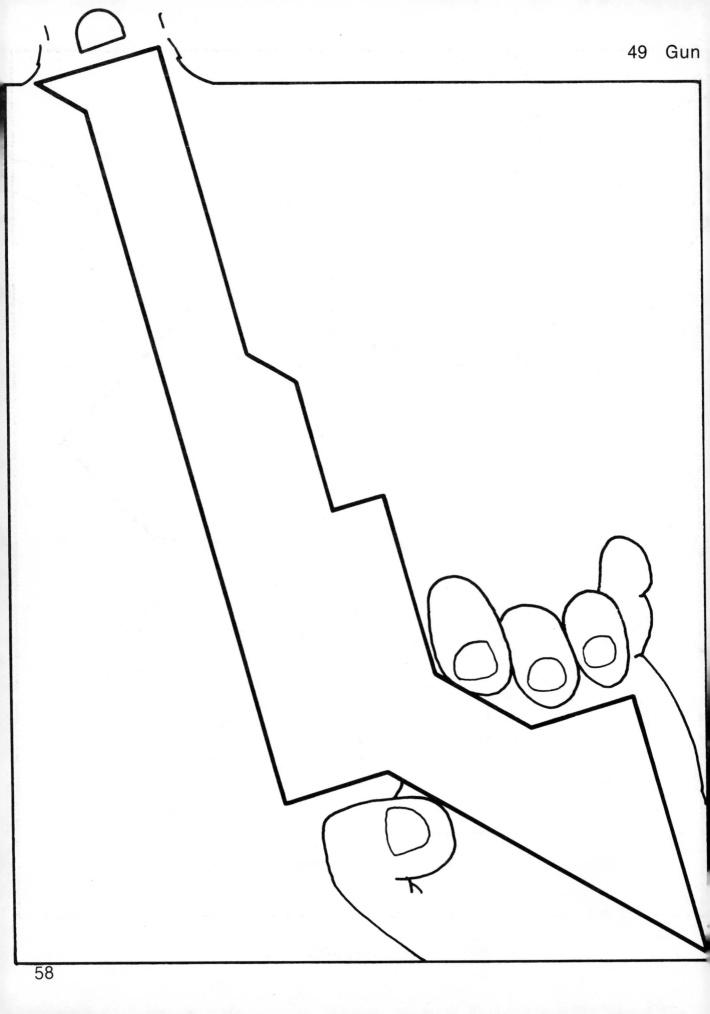

50   Butterfly

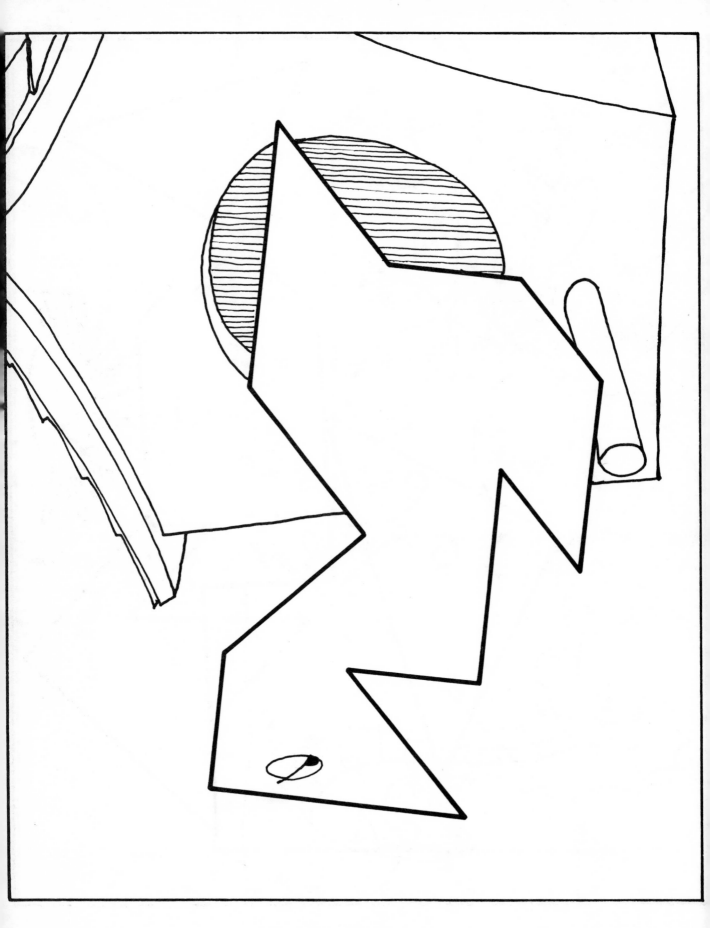

51   Pigeon

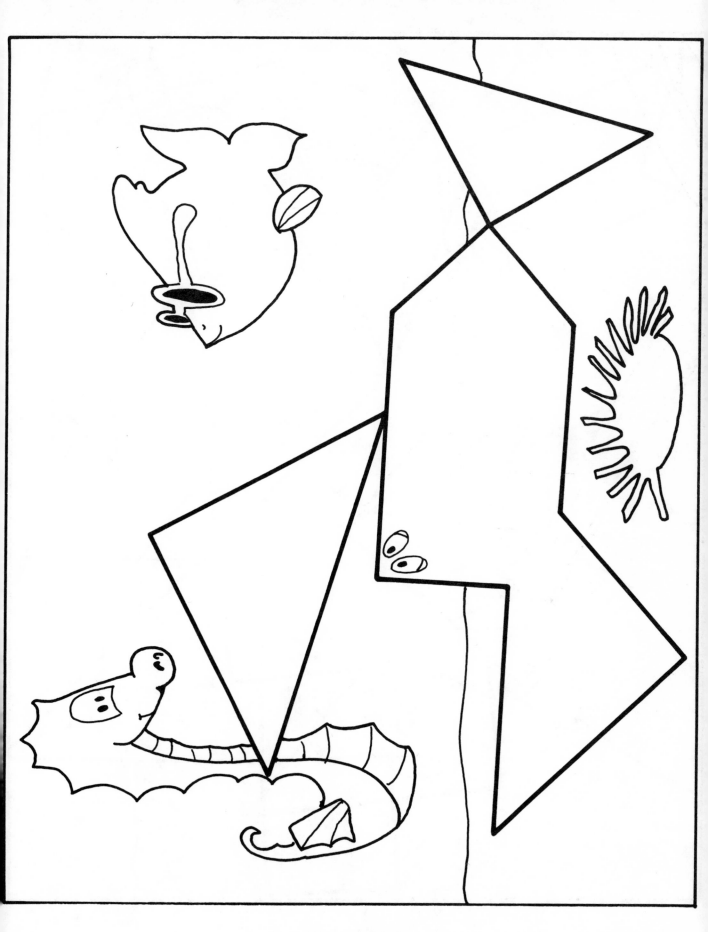

52 Lobster

53   Deer

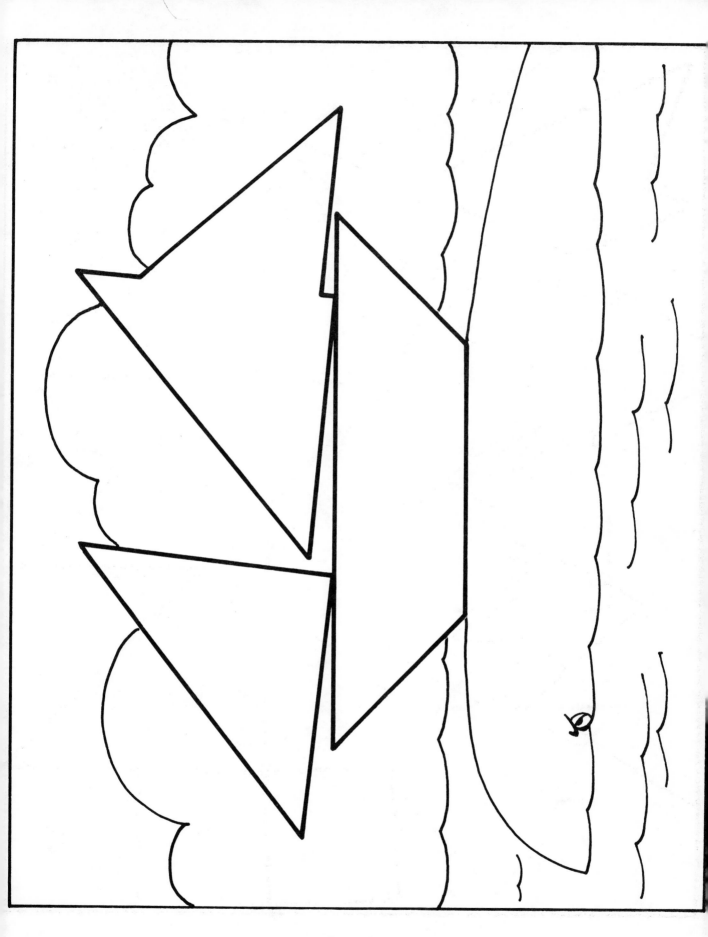

54 Ship

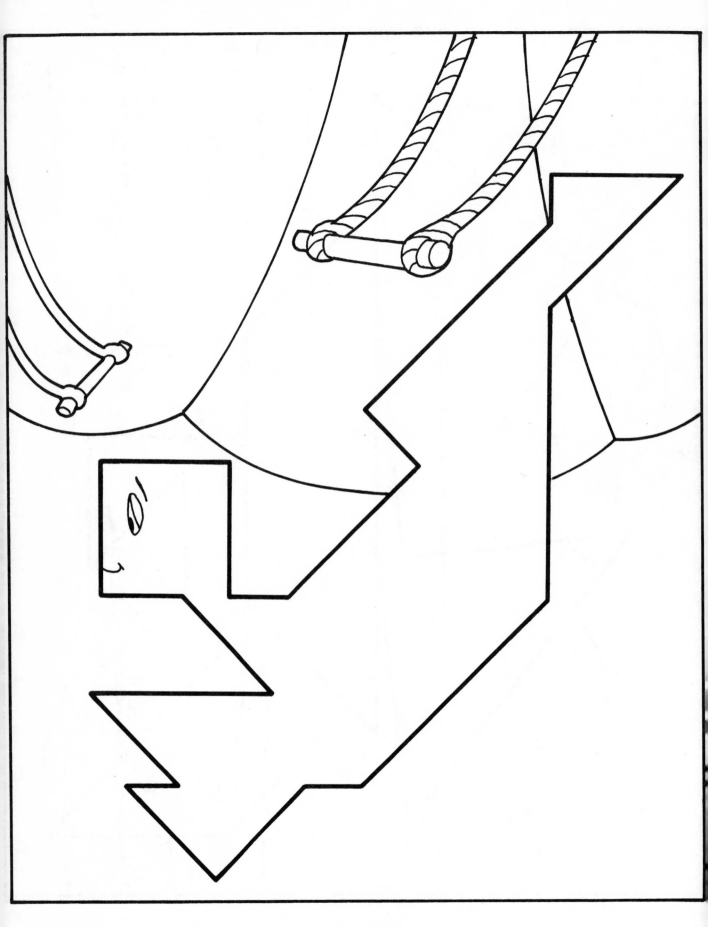

55 Acrobat

56 Robin

57 Woman

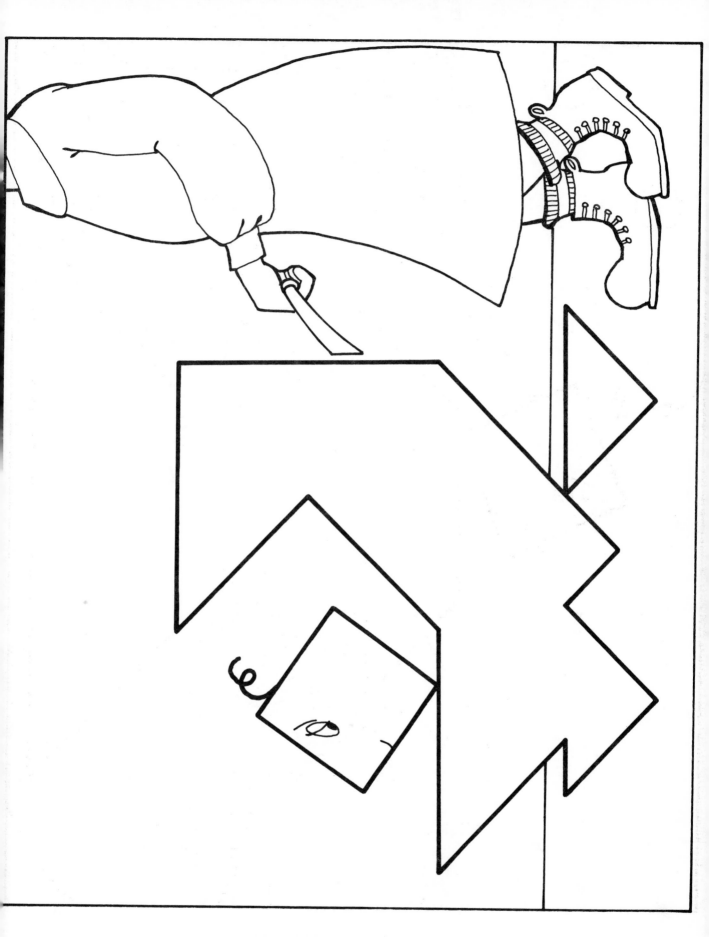

58 Baby in carriage

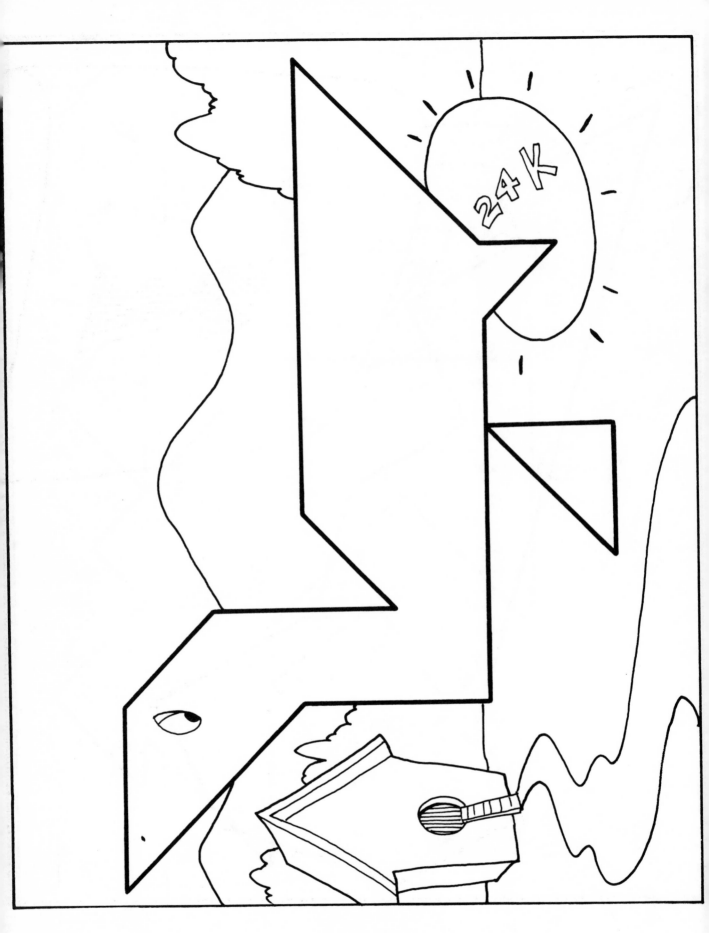

59 Goose

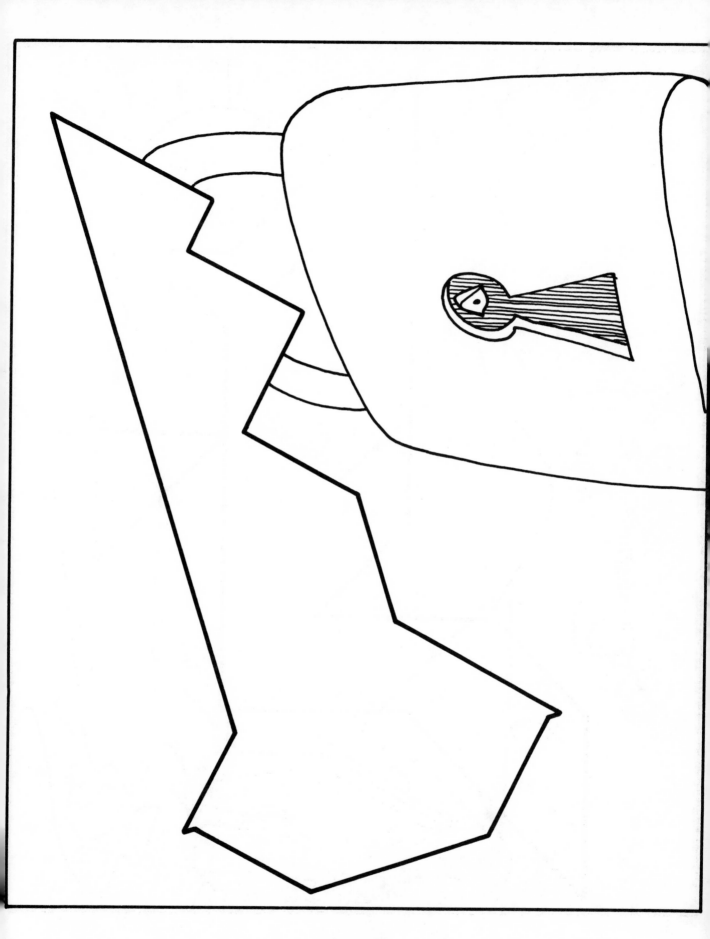

60   Key

61   Whale

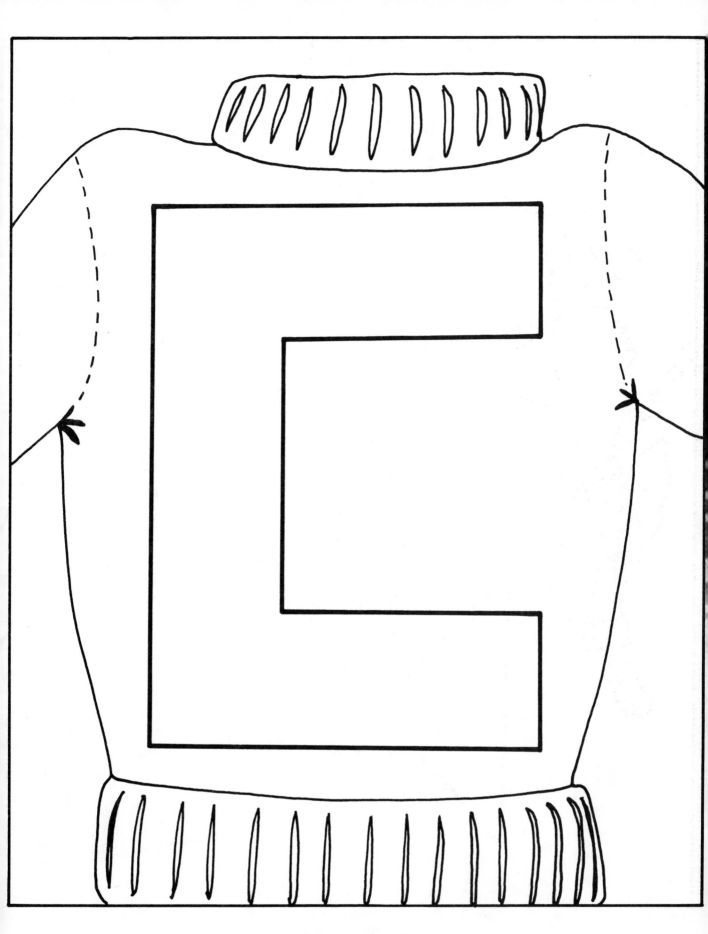

62 Letter C

63 Fish

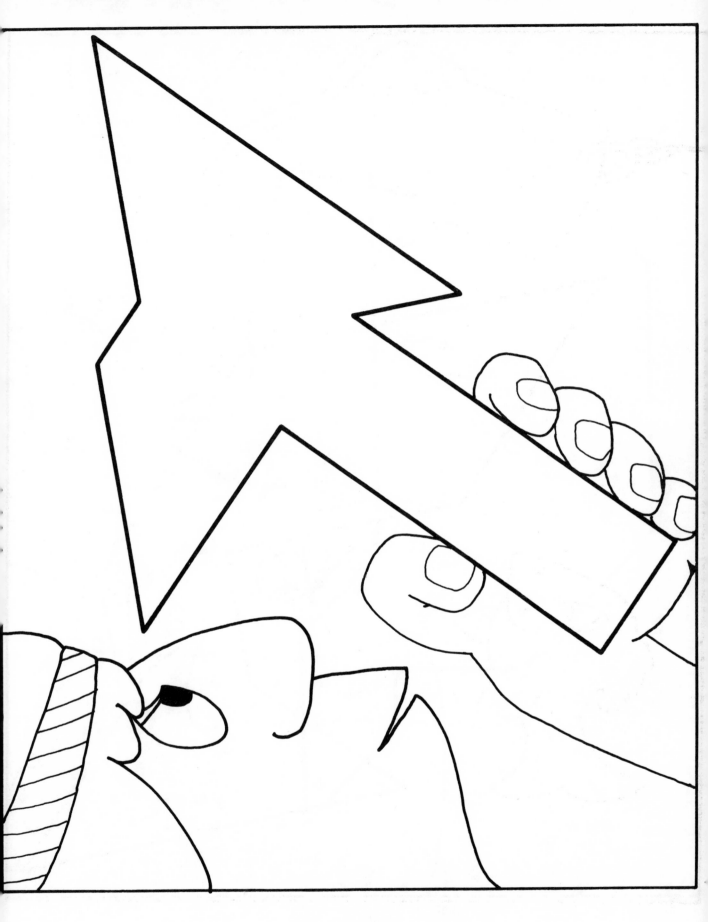

64 Hatchet

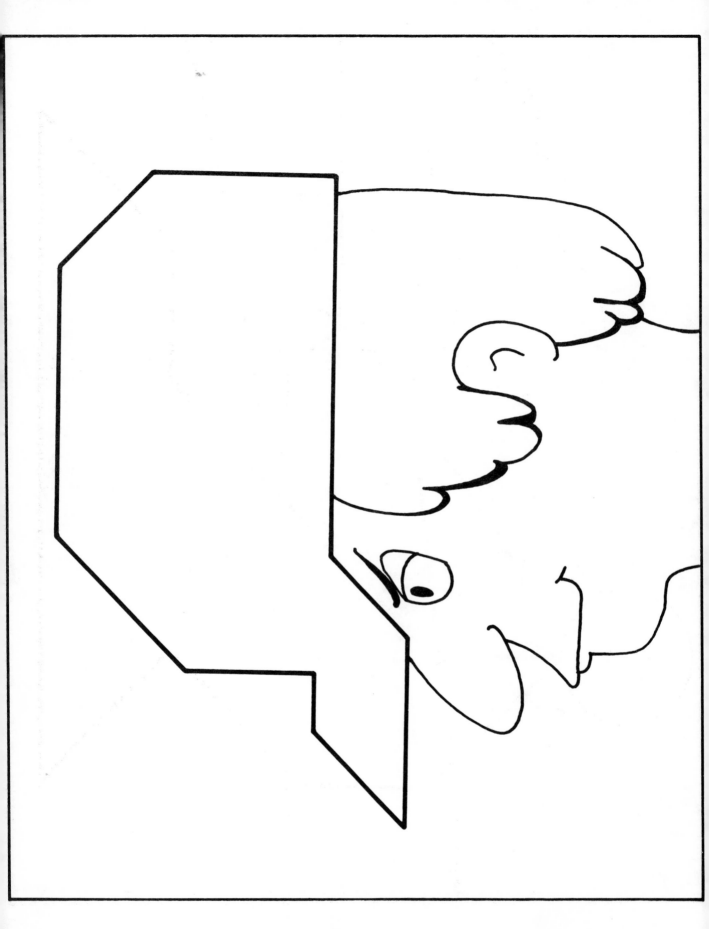

65 Cap

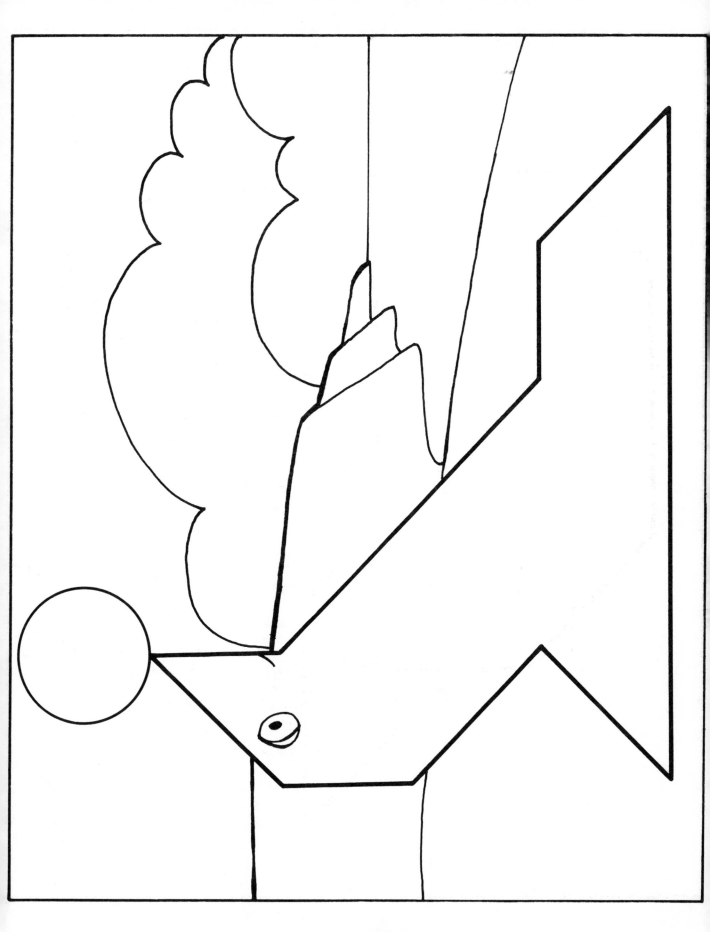

66 Seal

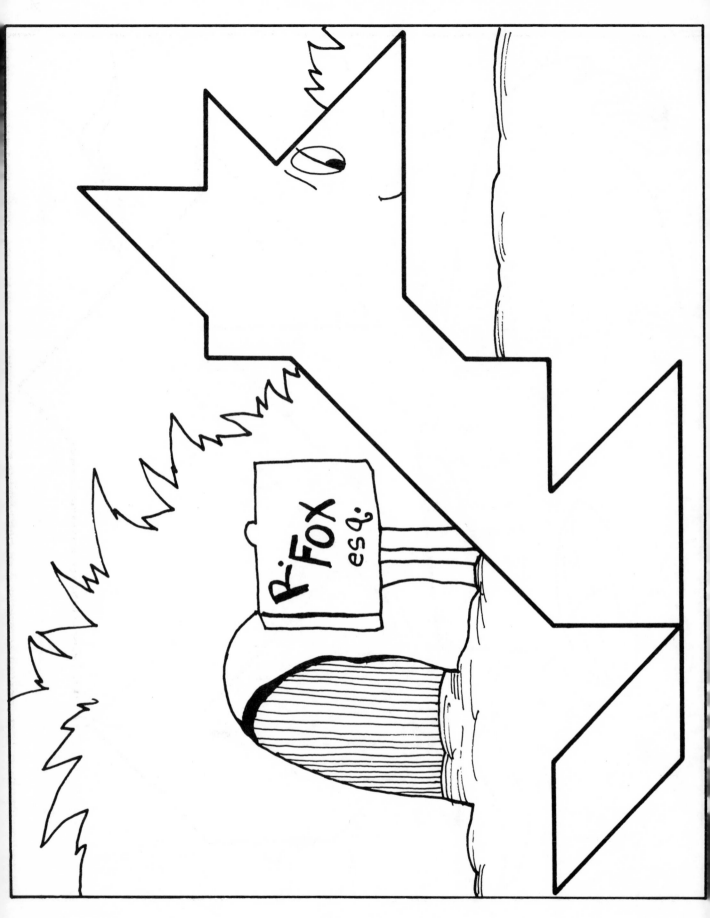

67 Fox

68 Seahorse

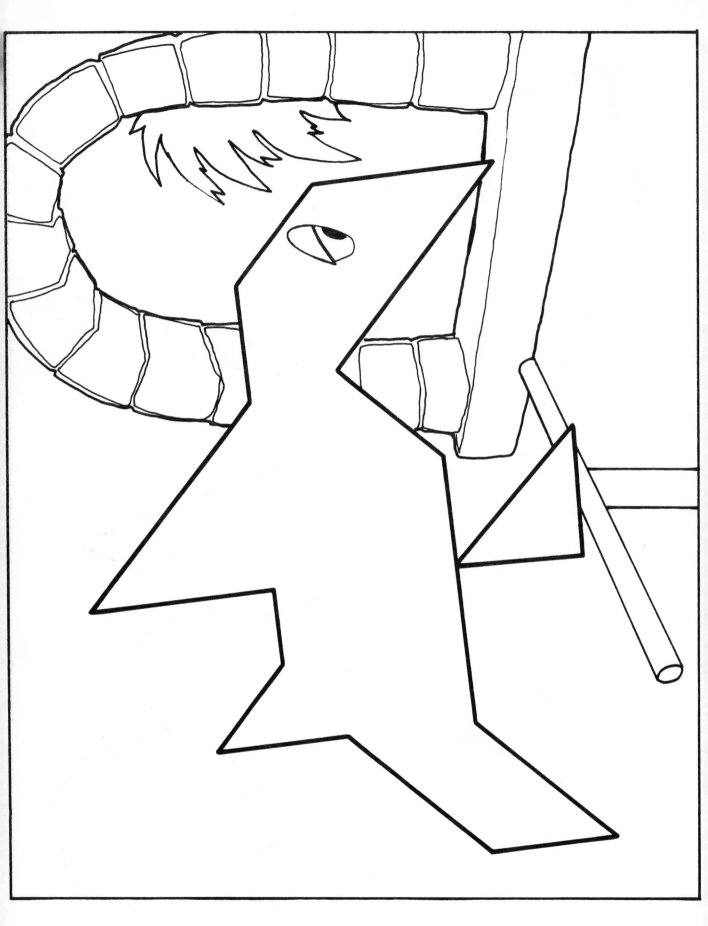

69 Parrot

70 Rocket

71 Duck

72   Boat

73 Shirt

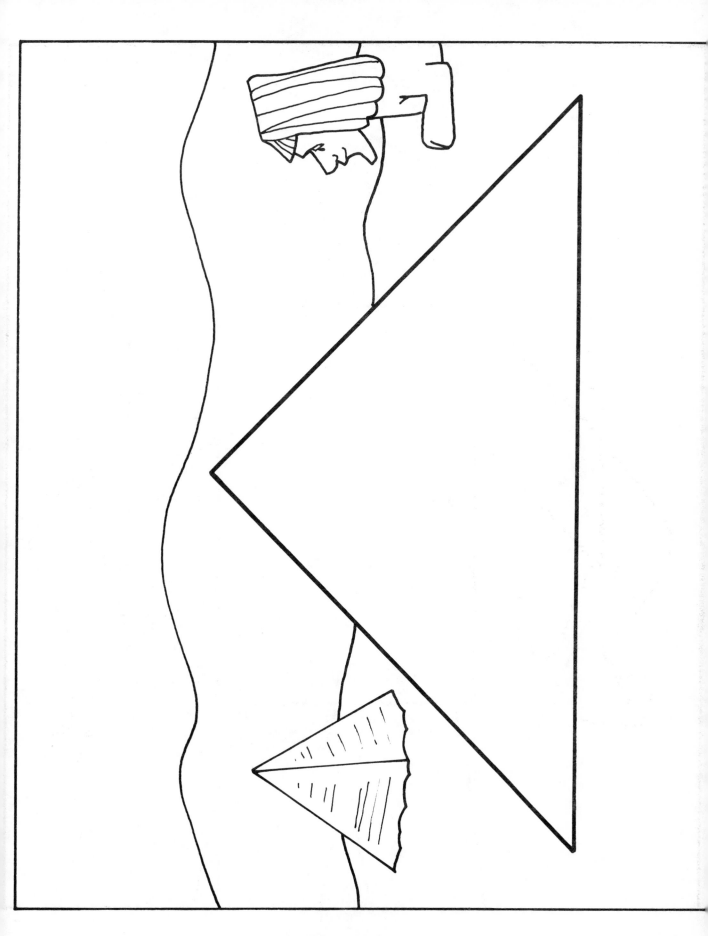

74 Triangle

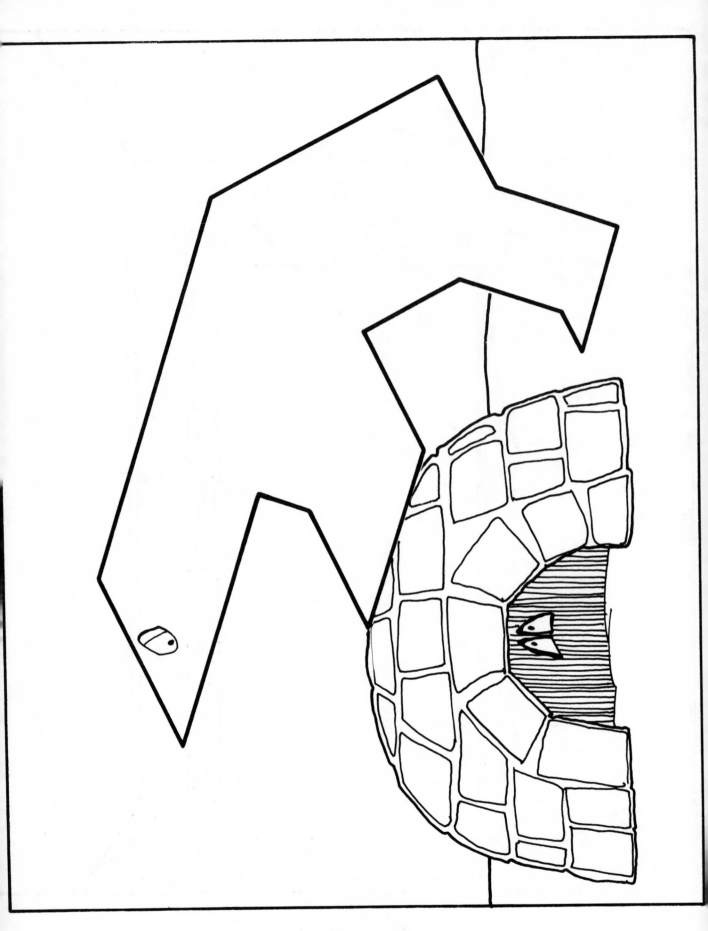

75 Polar bear

76　Rectangle

77   Monument

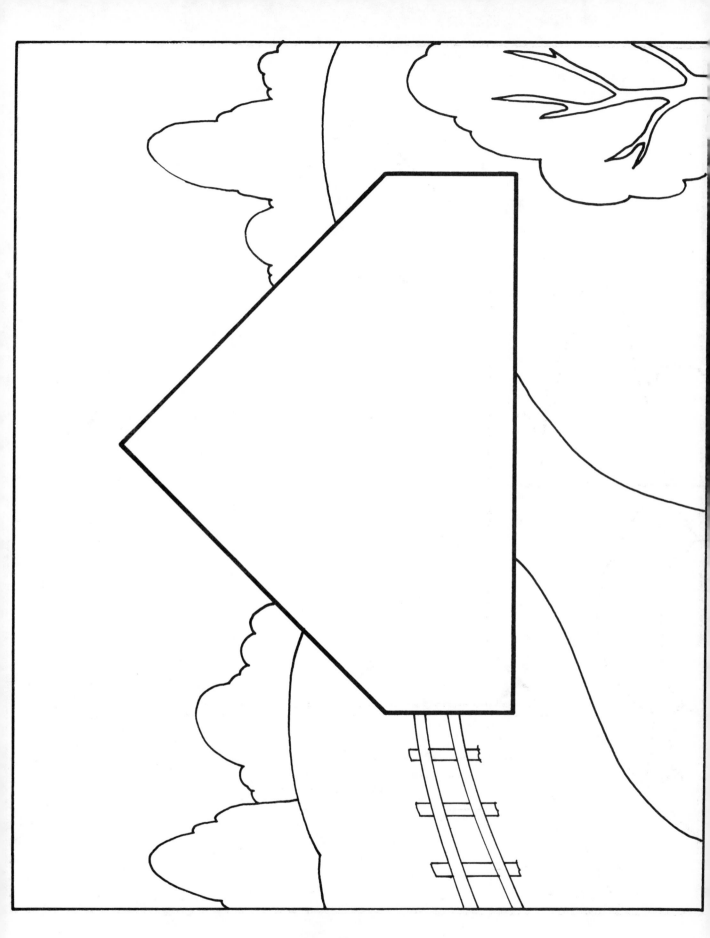

78   Pentagon

80   Colonial soldier

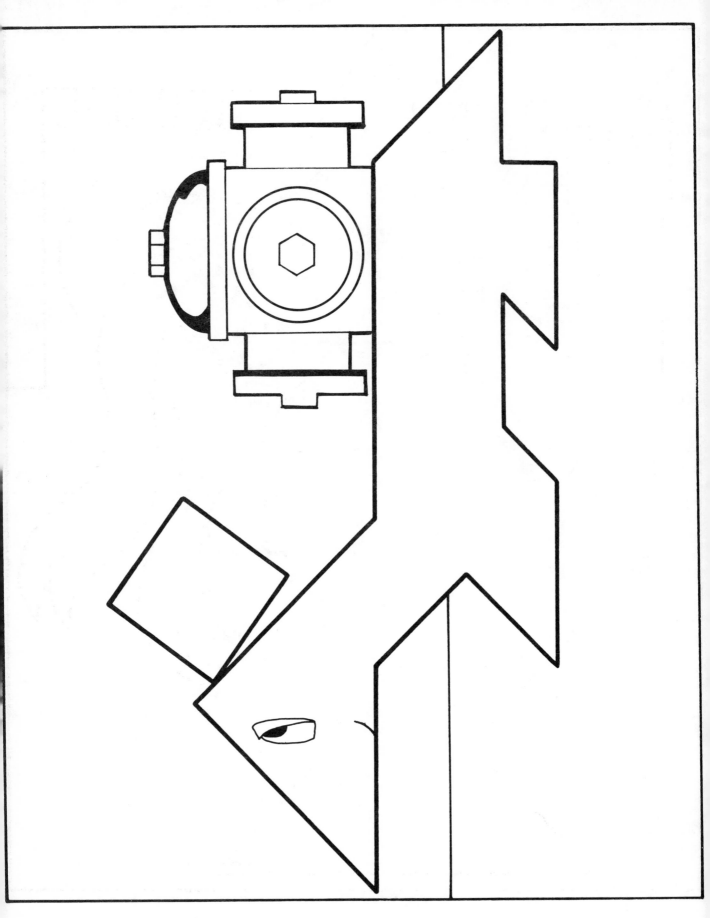

81 Dachshund

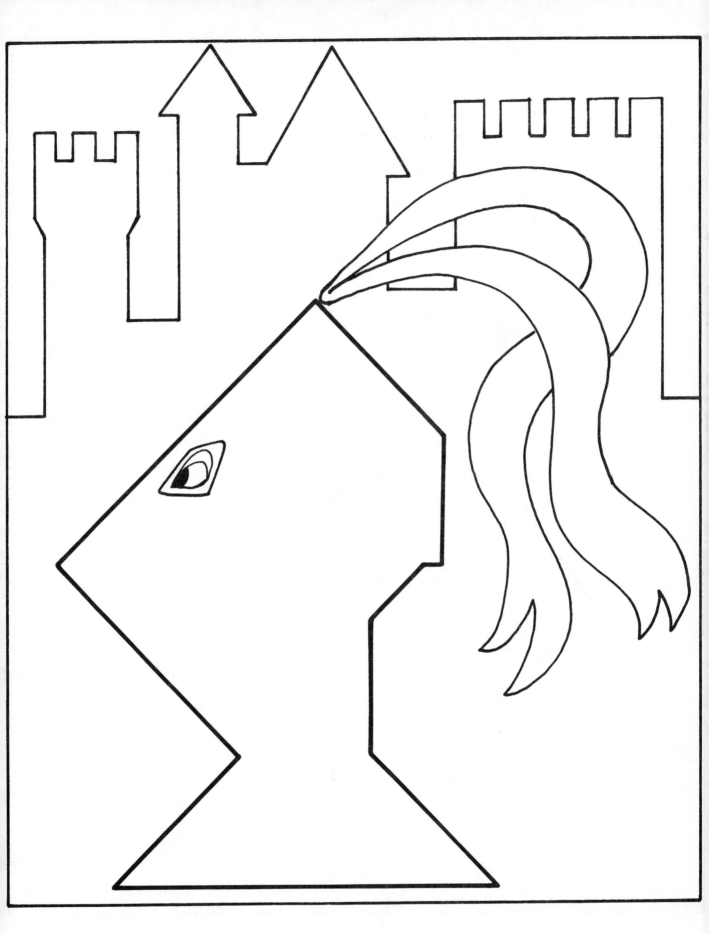

82 Knight

83 Lady

84 Square with gaps

85 Boot

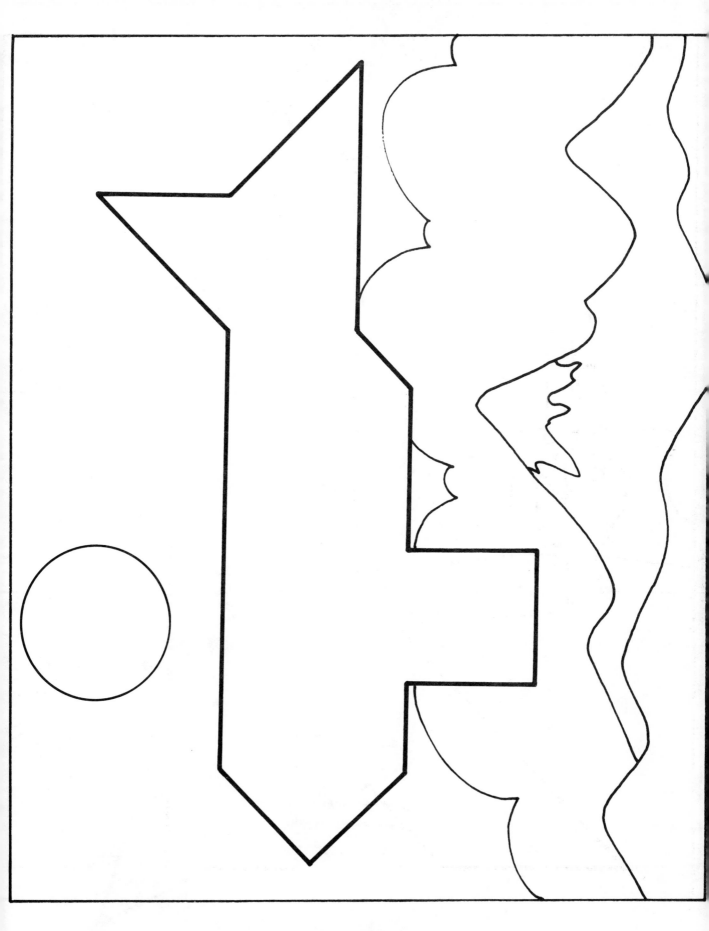

86   Blimp

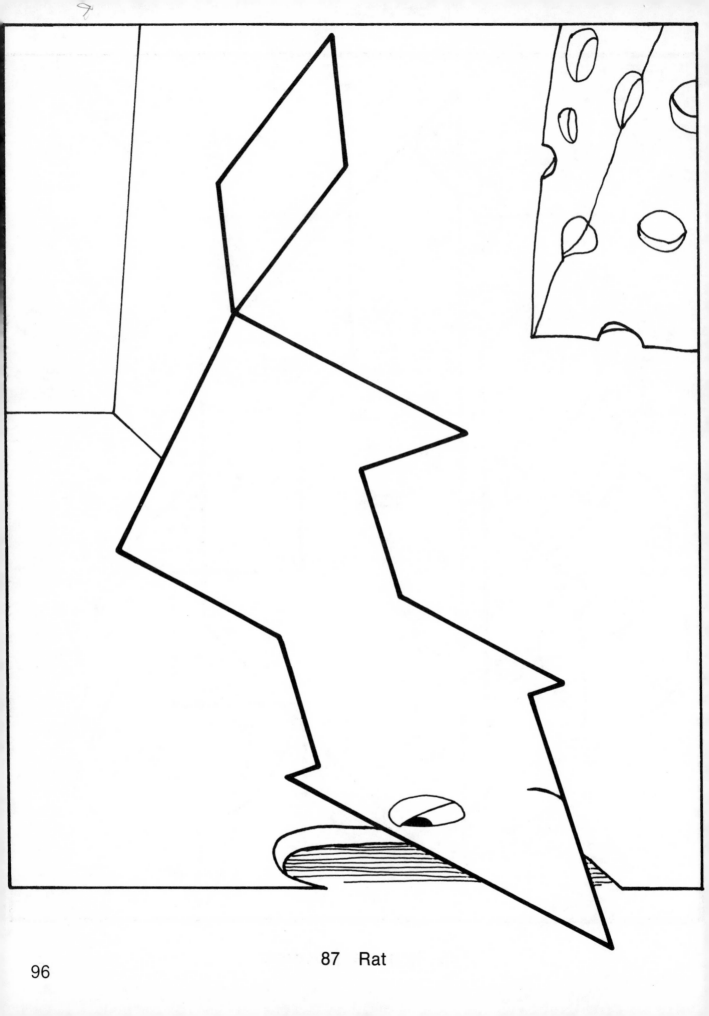

87   Rat

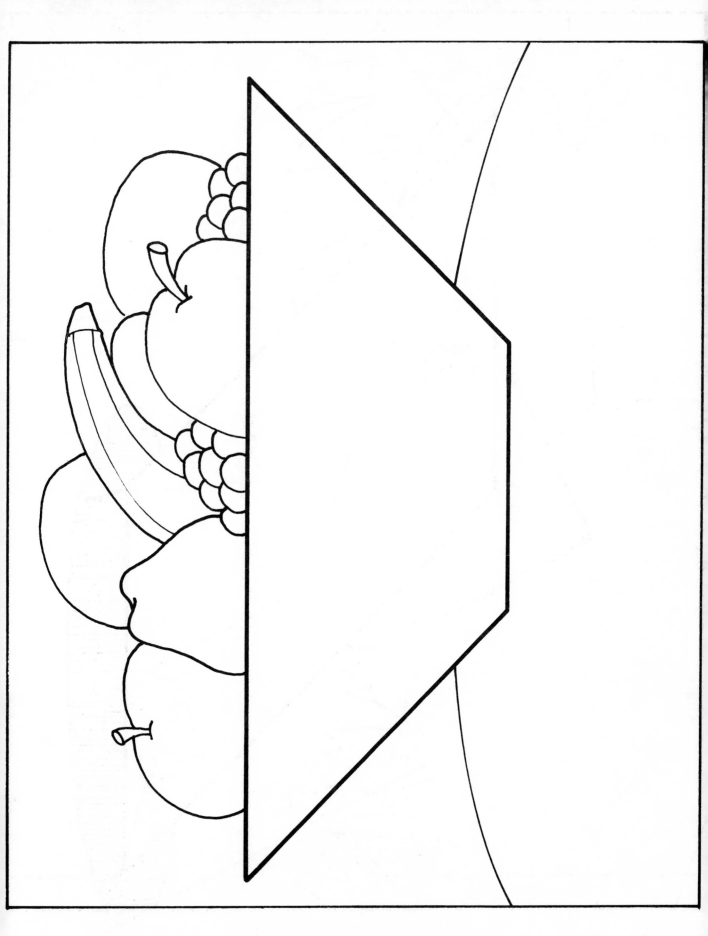

88   Isosceles trapezoid

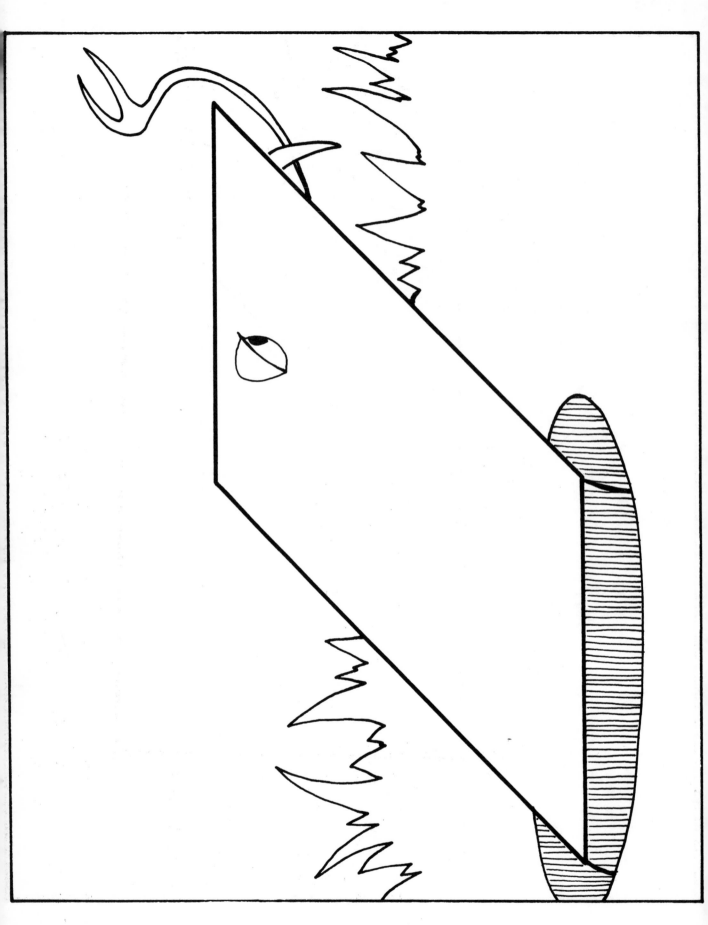

89 Parallelogram

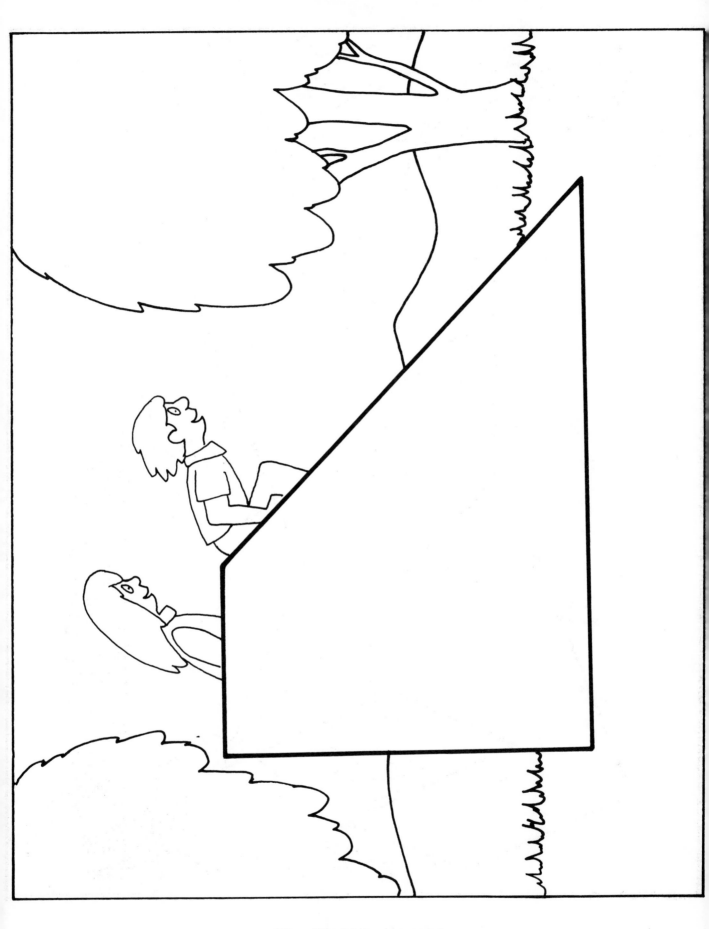

90   Right trapezoid

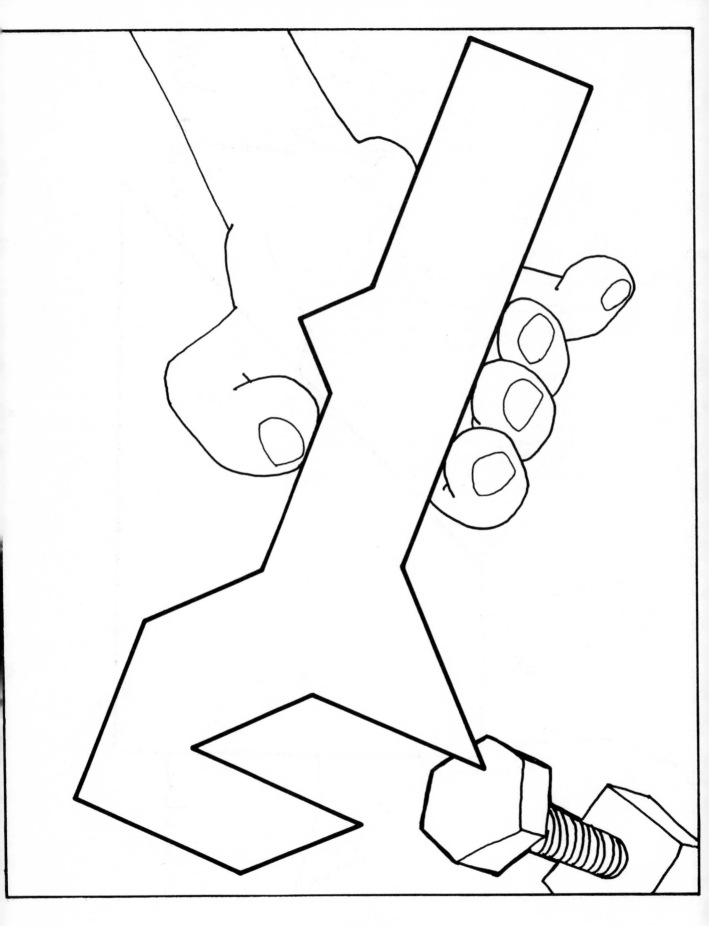

91 Wrench

TYPE IV

Tangram Patterns

Reduced tangram pattern outlines.

Contents

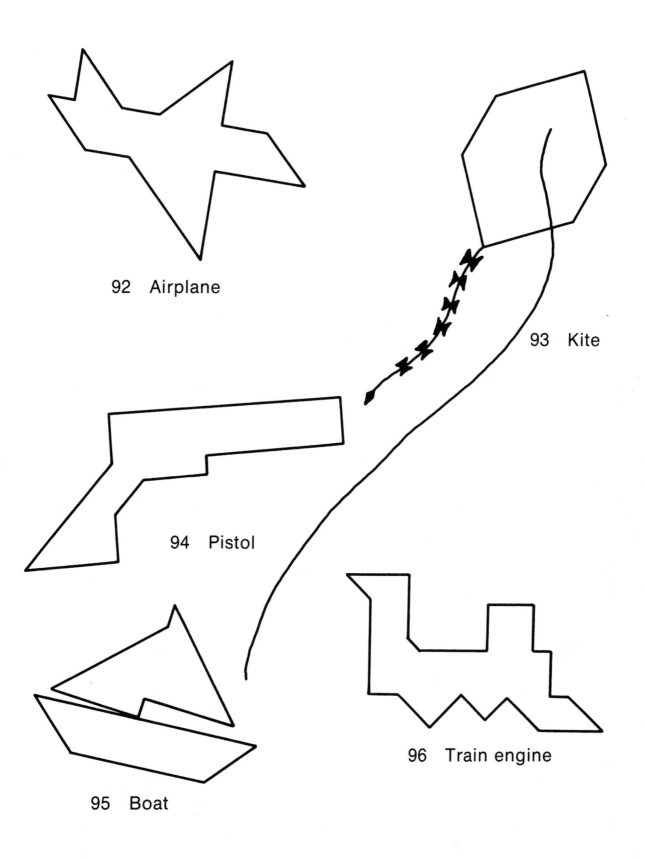

92   Airplane

93   Kite

94   Pistol

95   Boat

96   Train engine

97   Daniel Boone

98   Sitting Bull

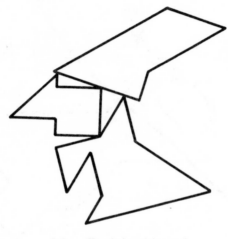

99   Robin Hood

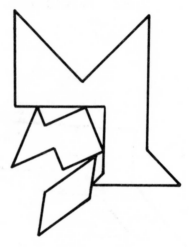

100   King Arthur

101   Eric the Red

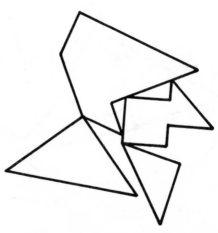

102   Robinson Crusoe

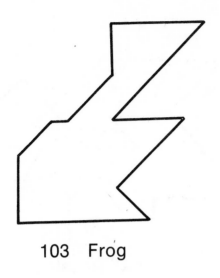

103 Frog

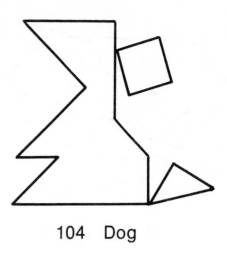

104 Dog

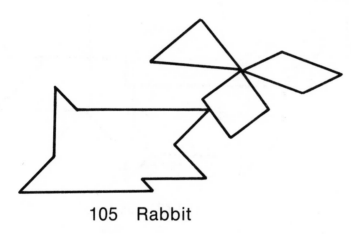

105 Rabbit

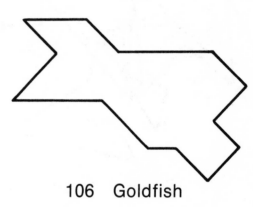

106 Goldfish

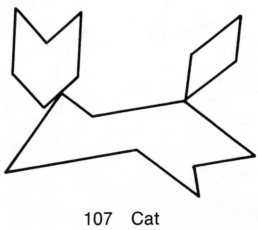

107 Cat

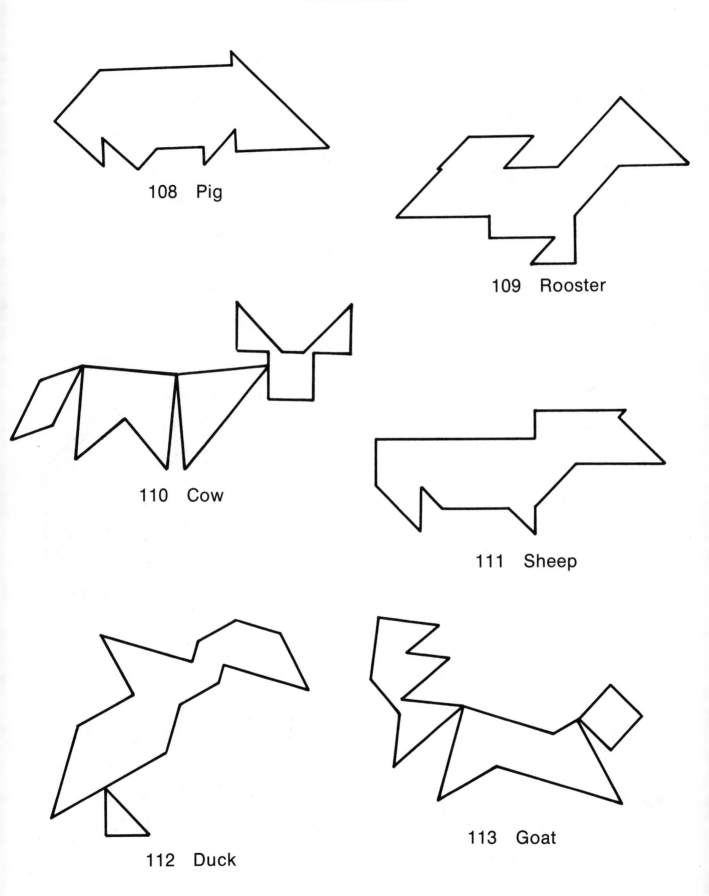

108 Pig

109 Rooster

110 Cow

111 Sheep

112 Duck

113 Goat

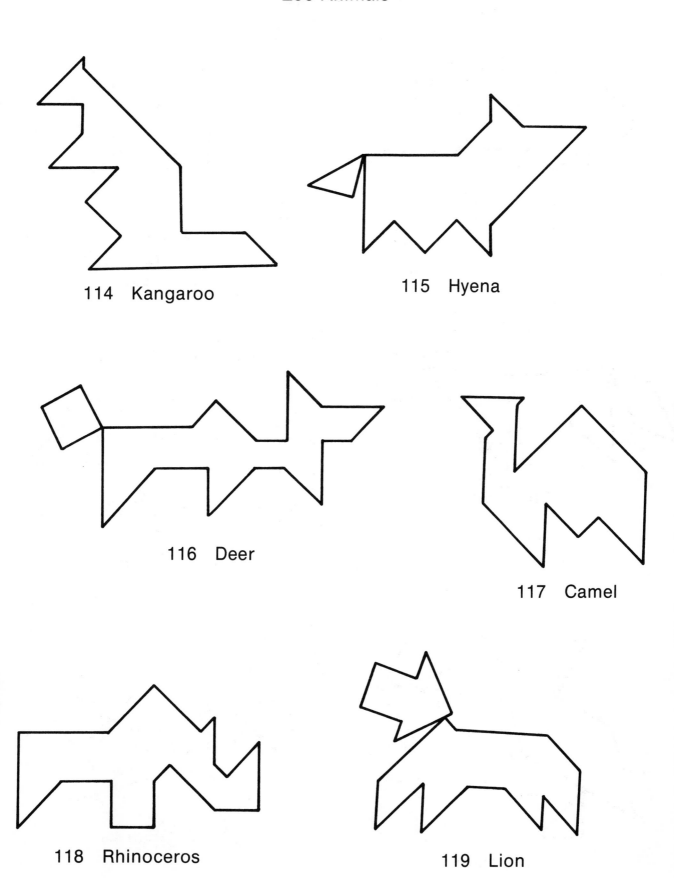

114 Kangaroo

115 Hyena

116 Deer

117 Camel

118 Rhinoceros

119 Lion

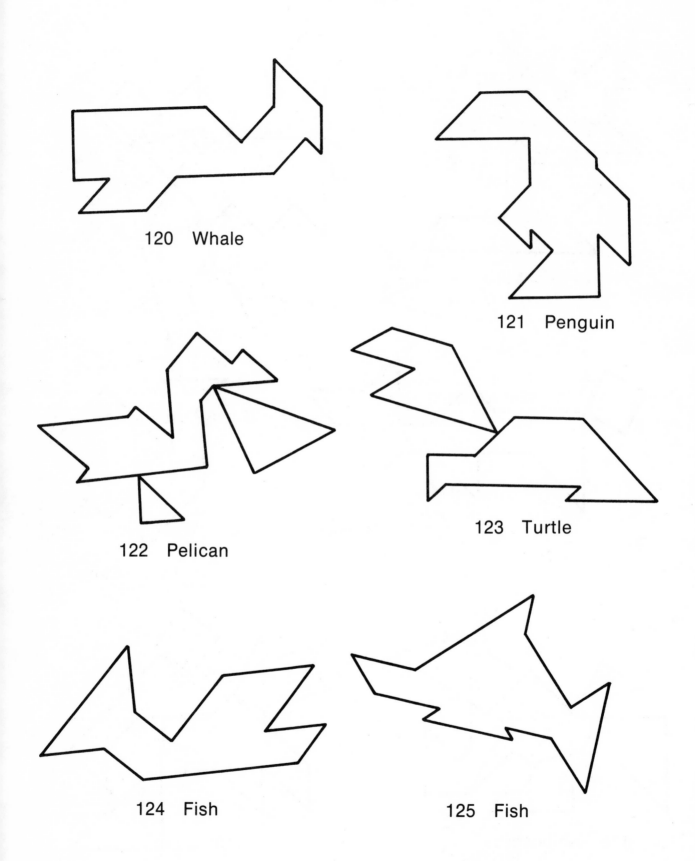

120   Whale

121   Penguin

122   Pelican

123   Turtle

124   Fish

125   Fish

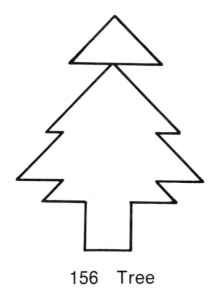

156   Tree

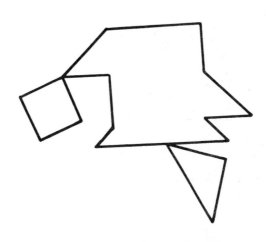

157   Santa Claus

158   Present

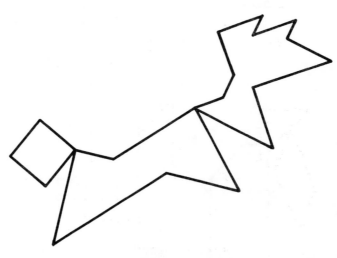

159   Reindeer

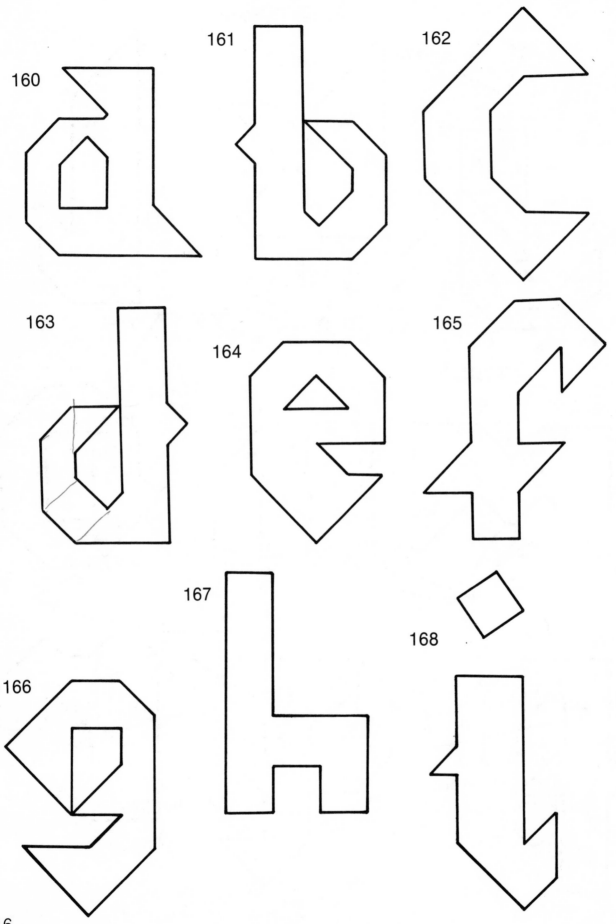

160

161

162

163

164

165

166

167

168

169 170 171

172 173 174

175 176 177

178

179

180

181

182

183

184

185

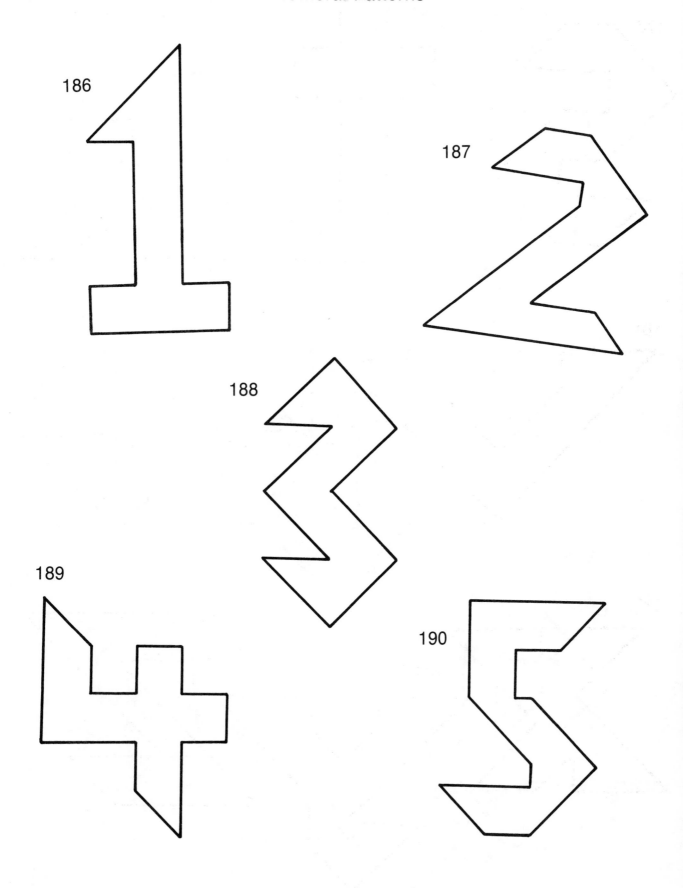

186

187

188

189

190

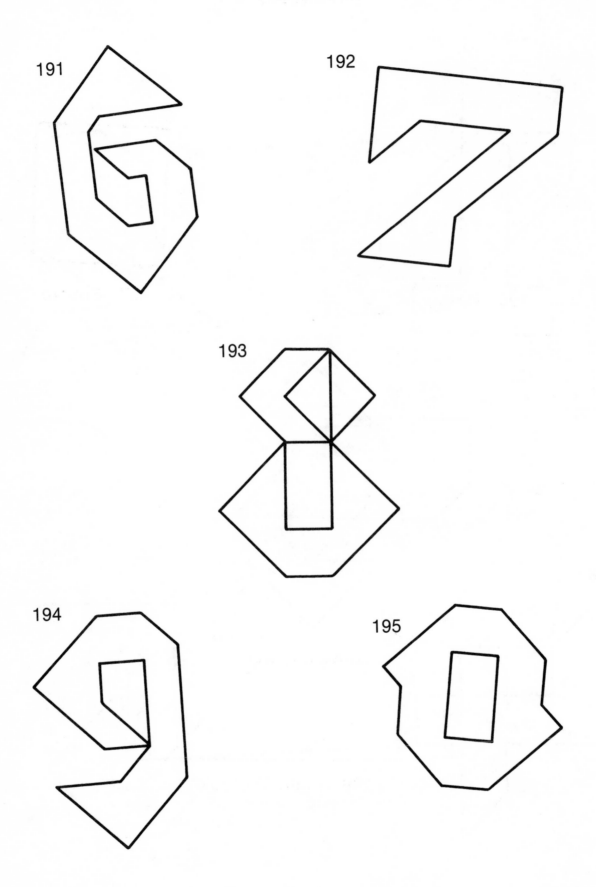

191

192

193

194

195

Polygons

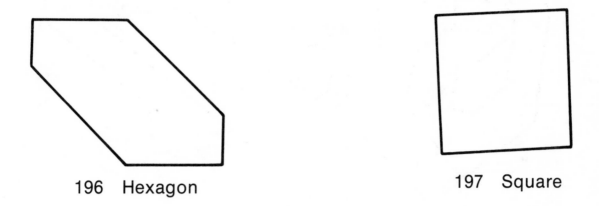

196   Hexagon

197   Square

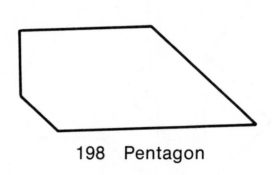

198   Pentagon

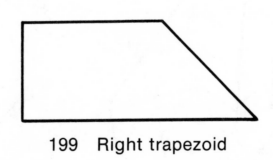

199   Right trapezoid

Double Tangrams

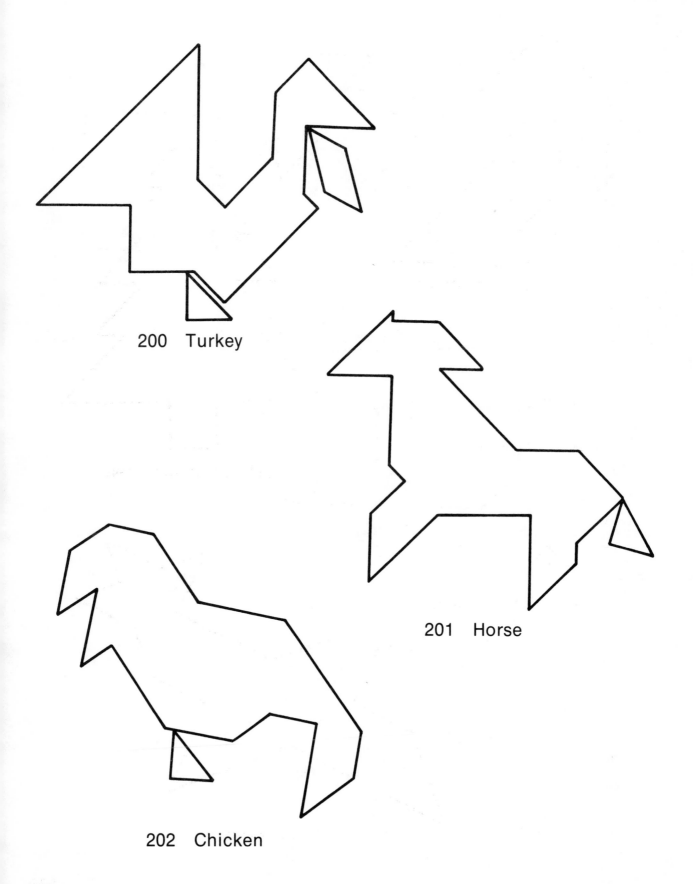

200 Turkey

201 Horse

202 Chicken

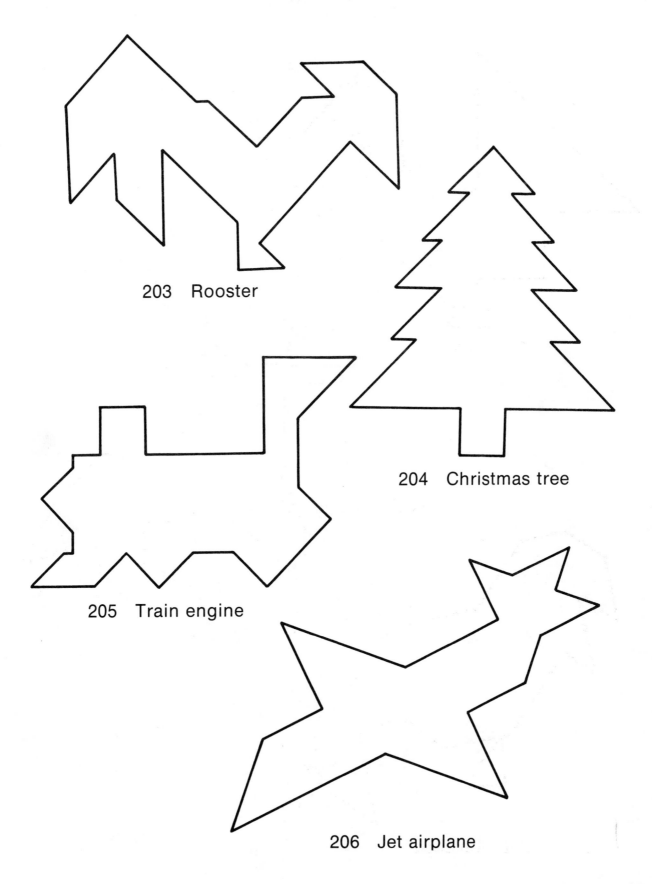

203   Rooster

204   Christmas tree

205   Train engine

206   Jet airplane

Double Tangrams

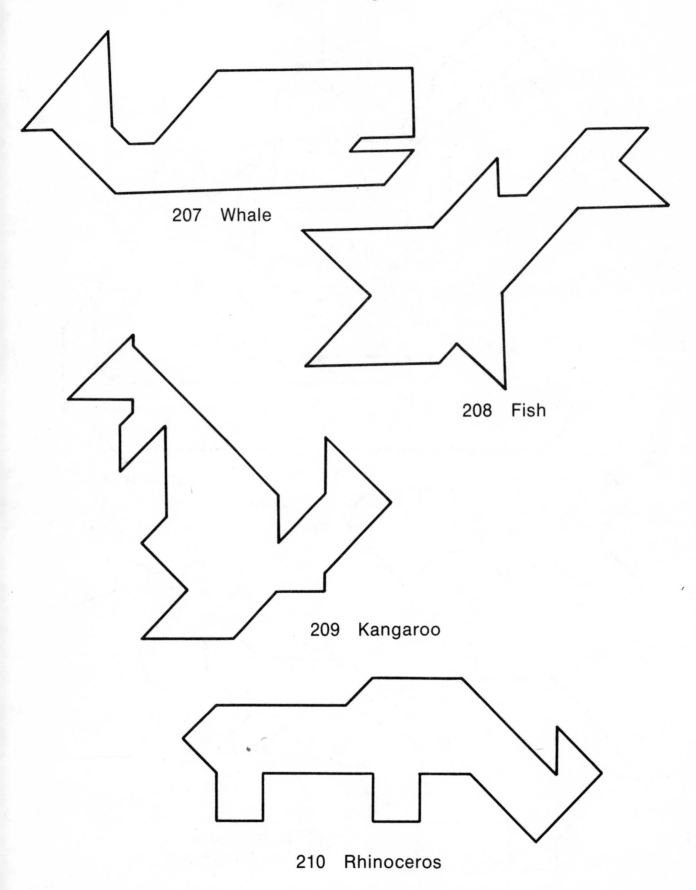

207 Whale

208 Fish

209 Kangaroo

210 Rhinoceros

Double Tangrams

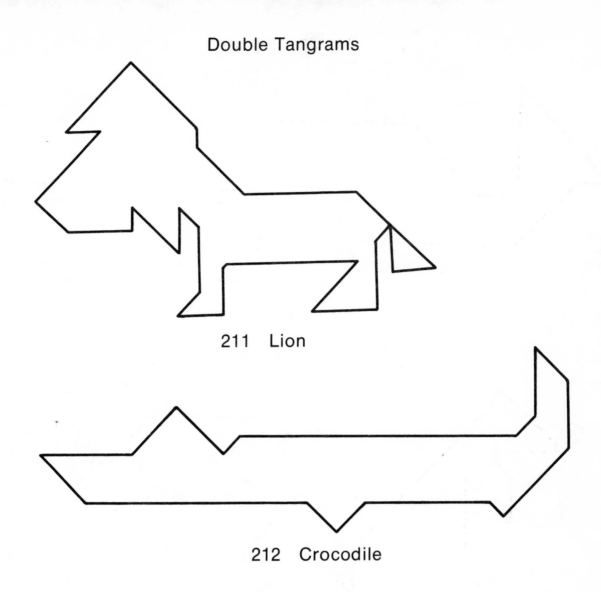

211   Lion

212   Crocodile

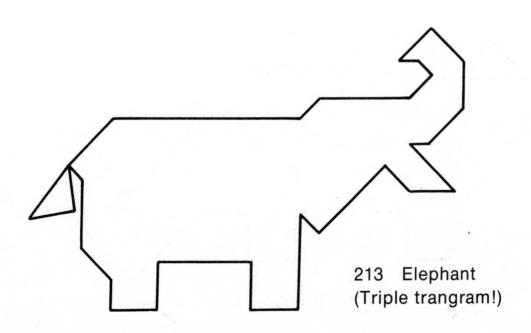

213   Elephant
(Triple trangram!)

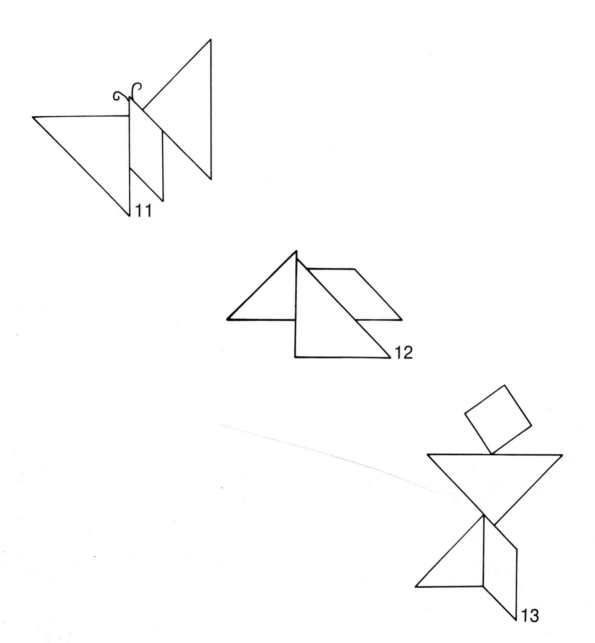

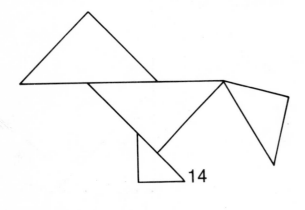

14

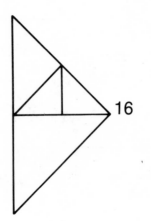

16

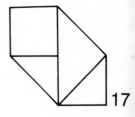

17

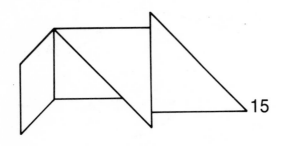

15

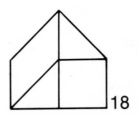

18

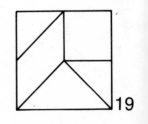

19

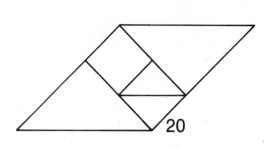

20

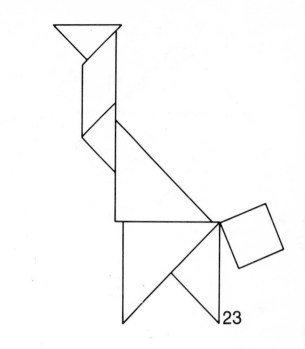

23

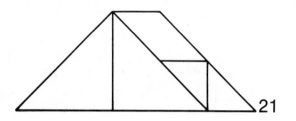

21

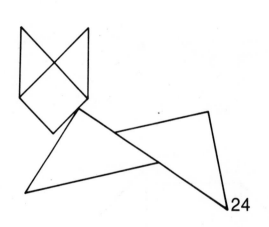

24

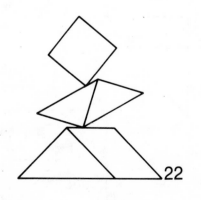

22

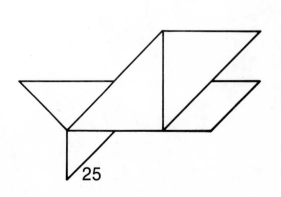

25

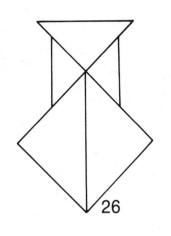

26

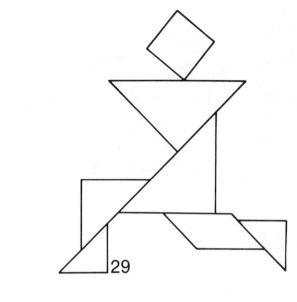

29

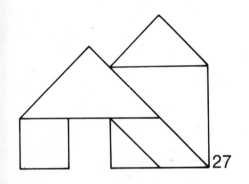

27

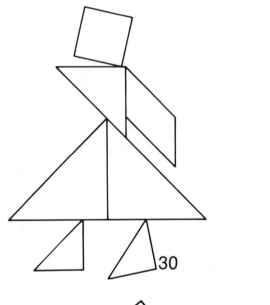

30

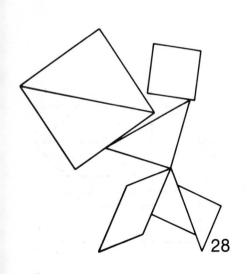

28

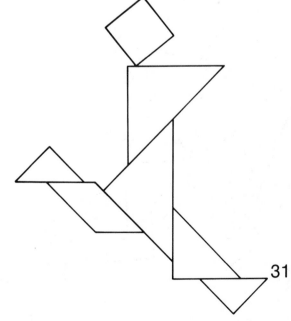

31

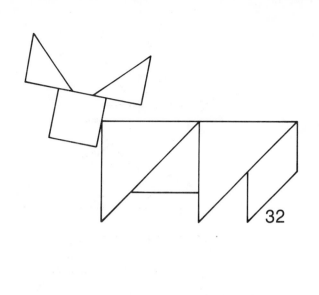

32

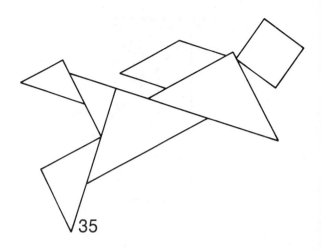

35

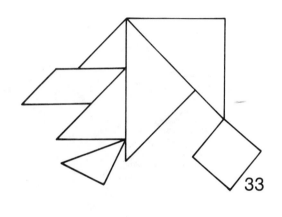

33

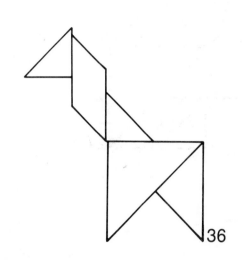

36

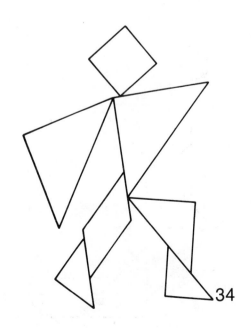

34

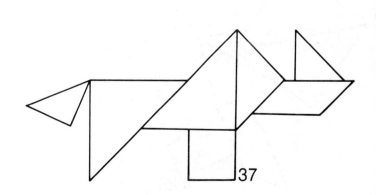

37

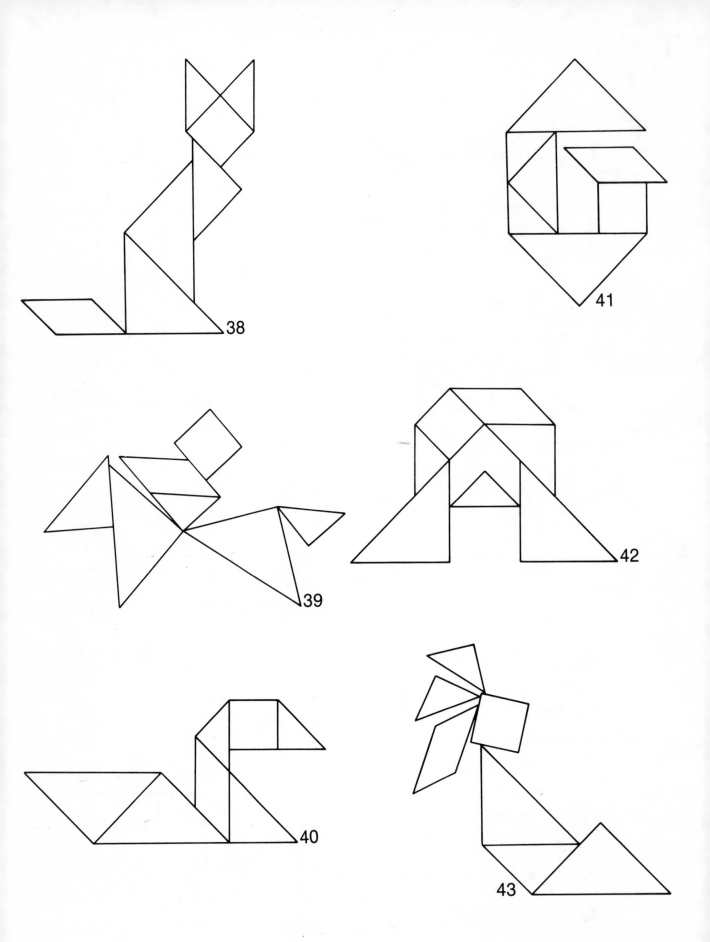

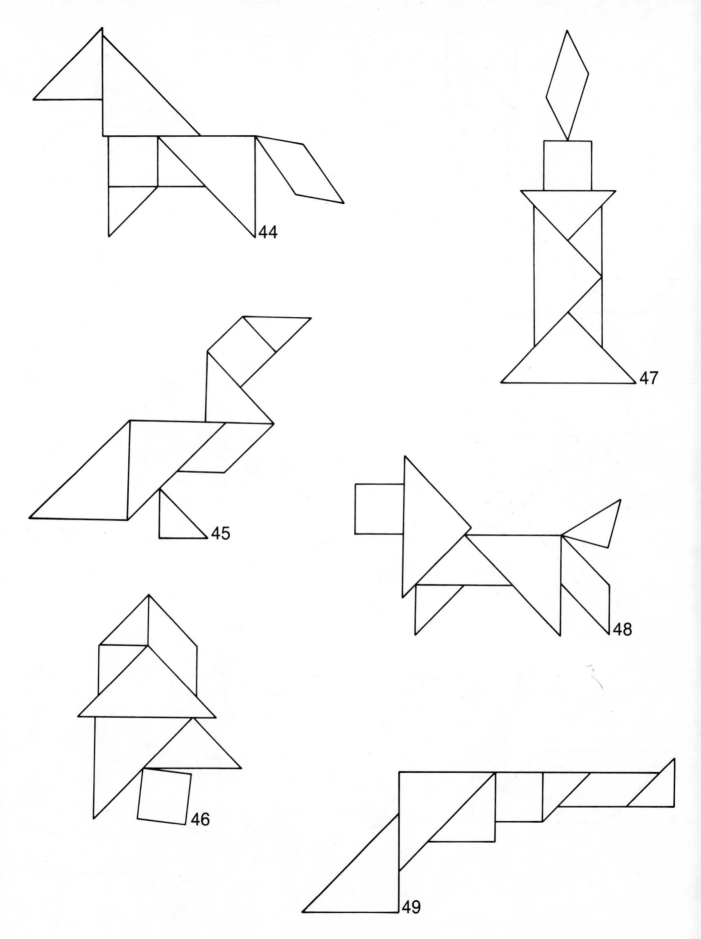

44

47

45

46

48

49

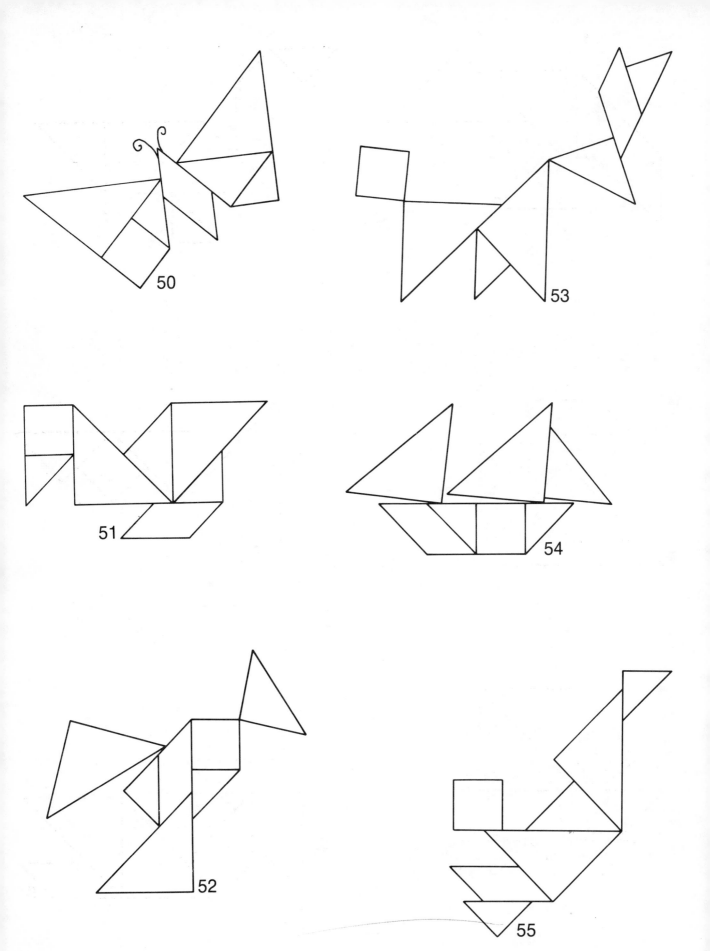

50

53

51

54

52

55

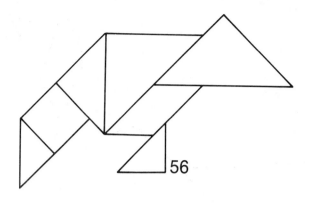

56

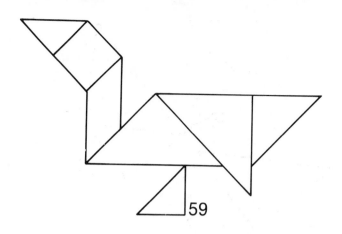

59

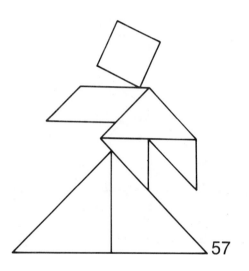

57

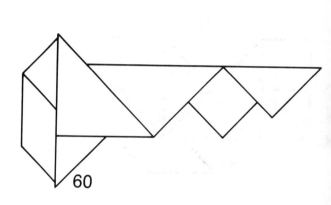

60

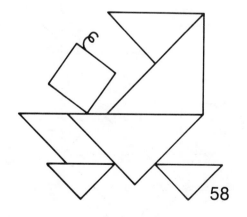

58

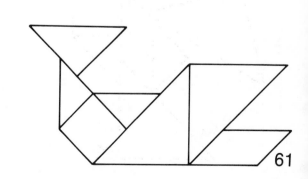

61

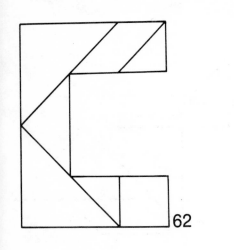

62

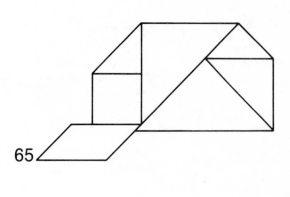

65

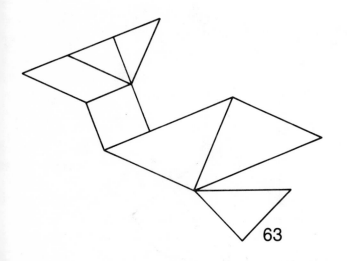

63

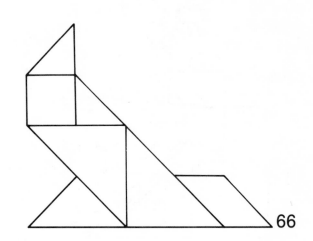

66

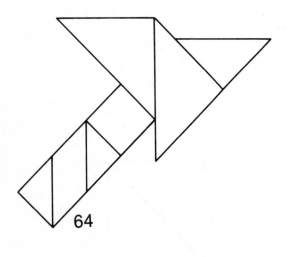

64

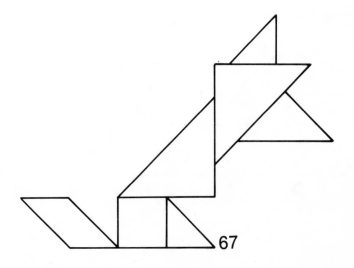

67

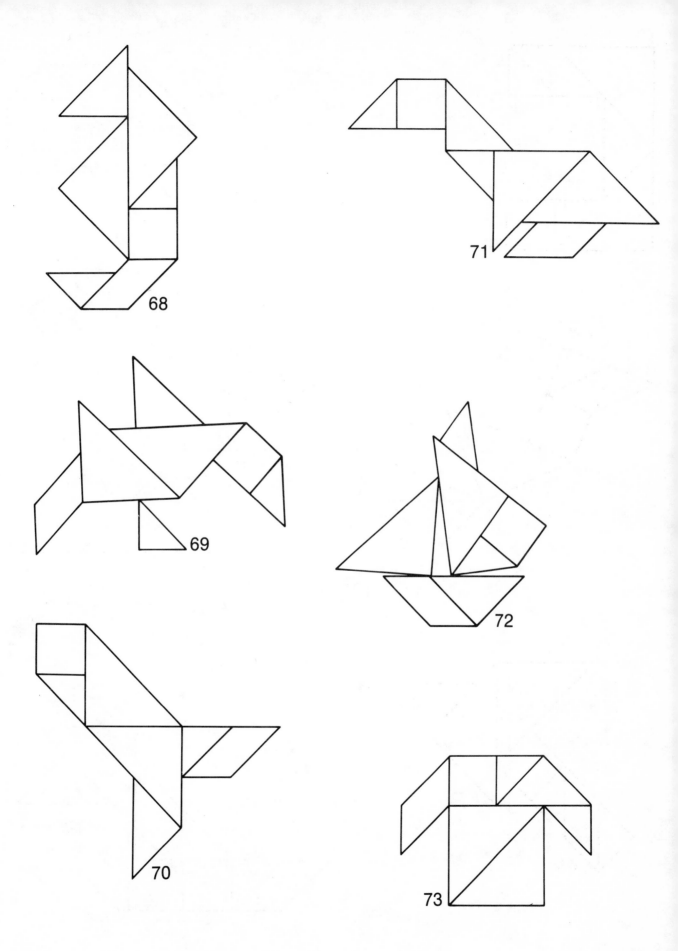

68

71

69

72

70

73

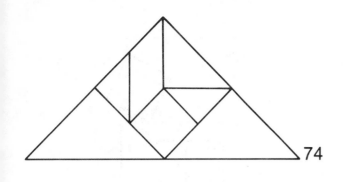 74

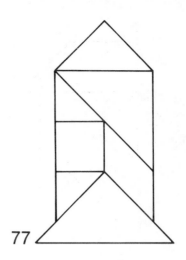 77

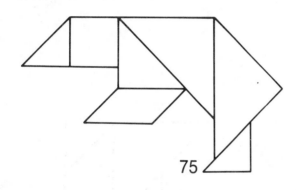 75

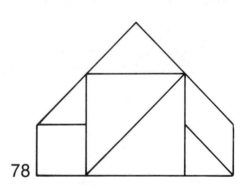 78

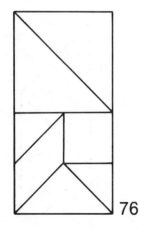 76

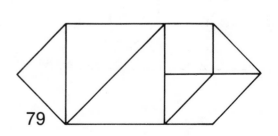 79

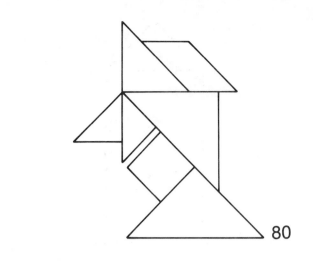

80

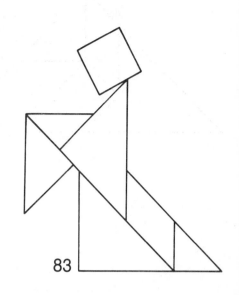

83

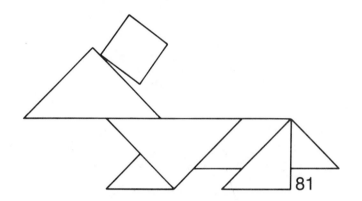

81

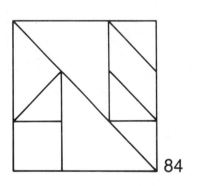

84

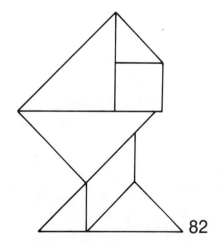

82

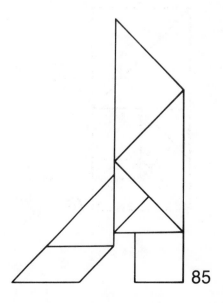

85

139

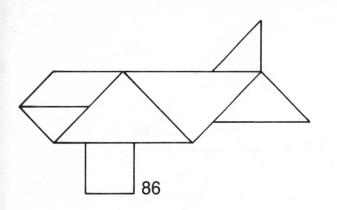

86

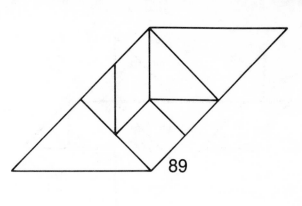

89

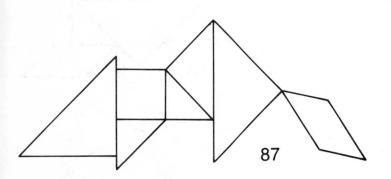

87

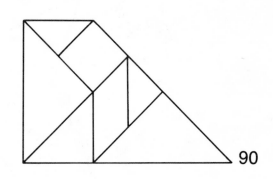

90

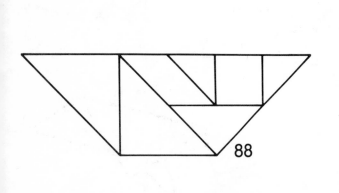

88

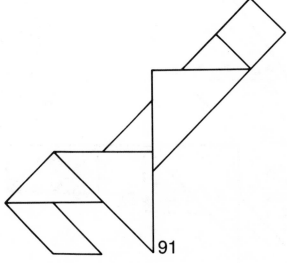

91

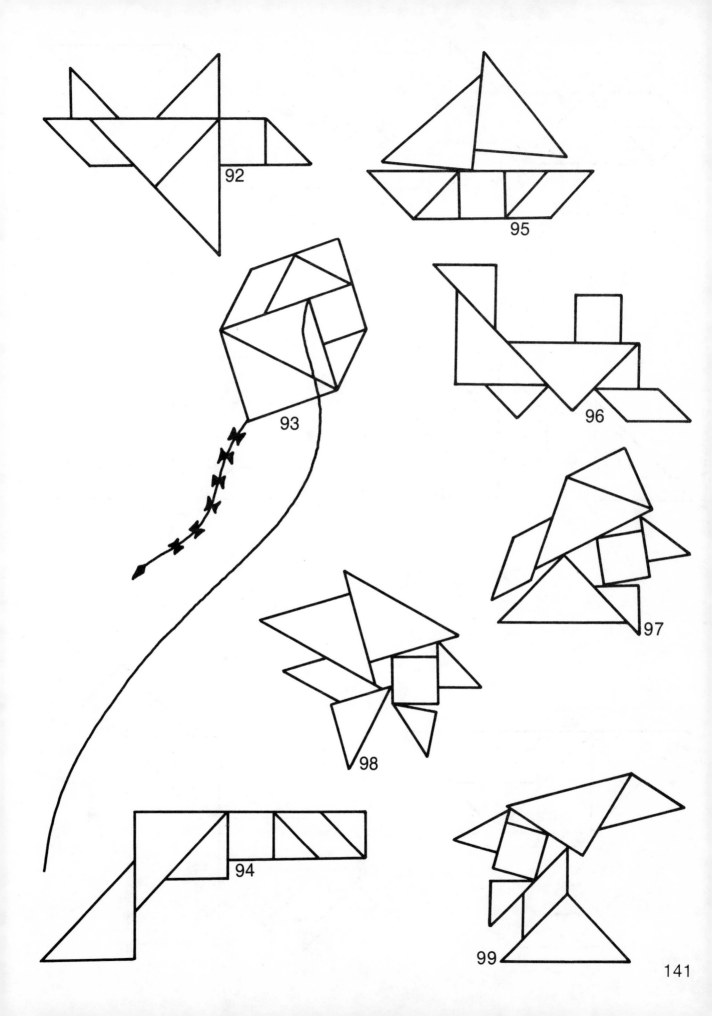

92

95

93

96

97

98

94

99

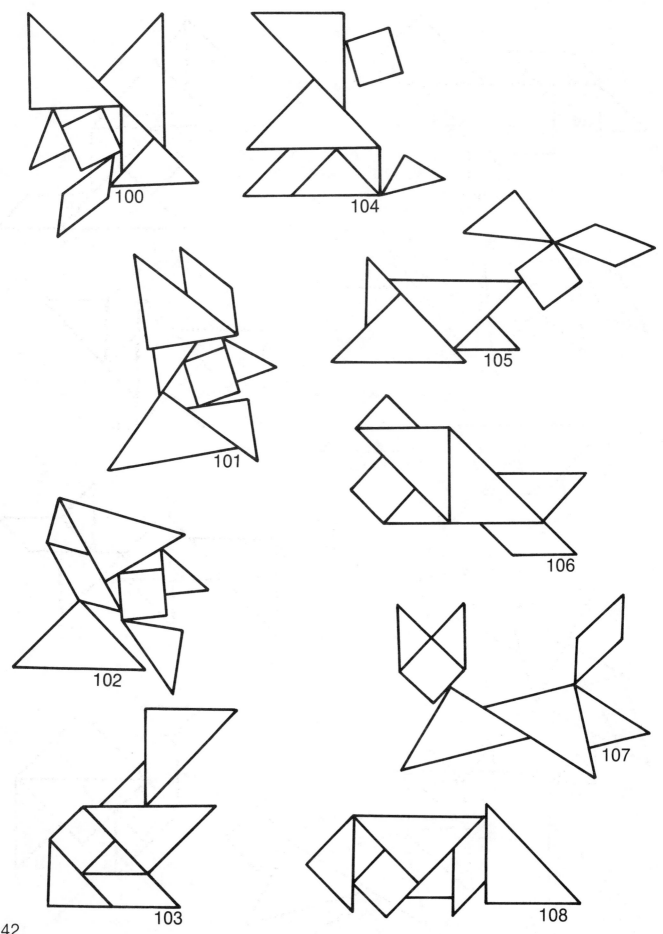

100

104

101

105

102

106

103

107

108

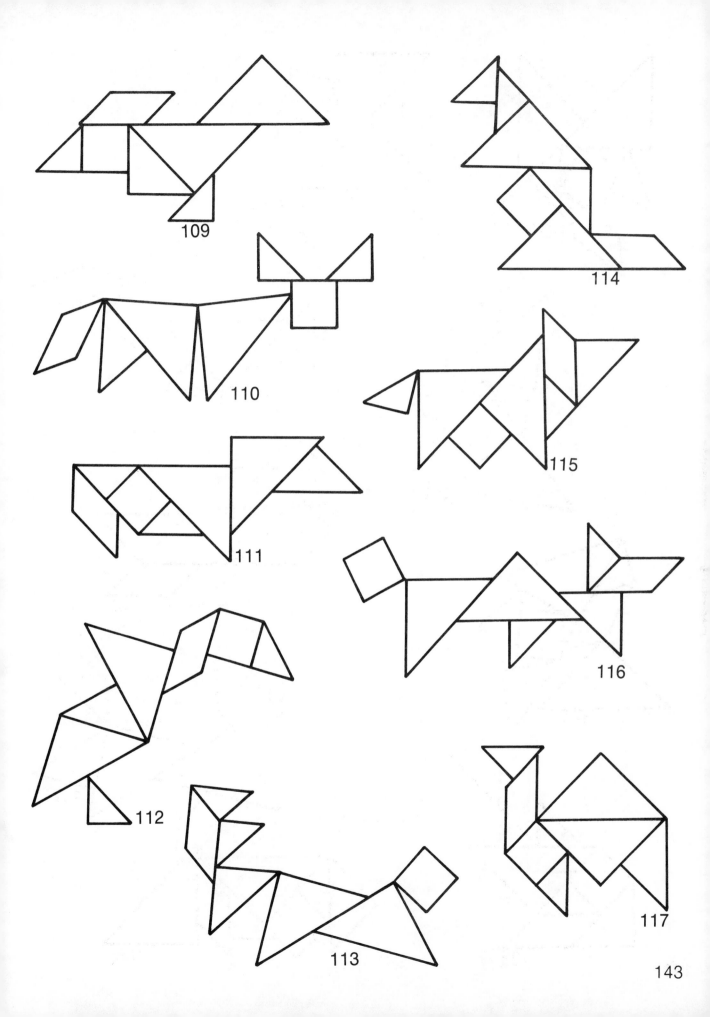

109

114

110

115

111

112

116

113

117

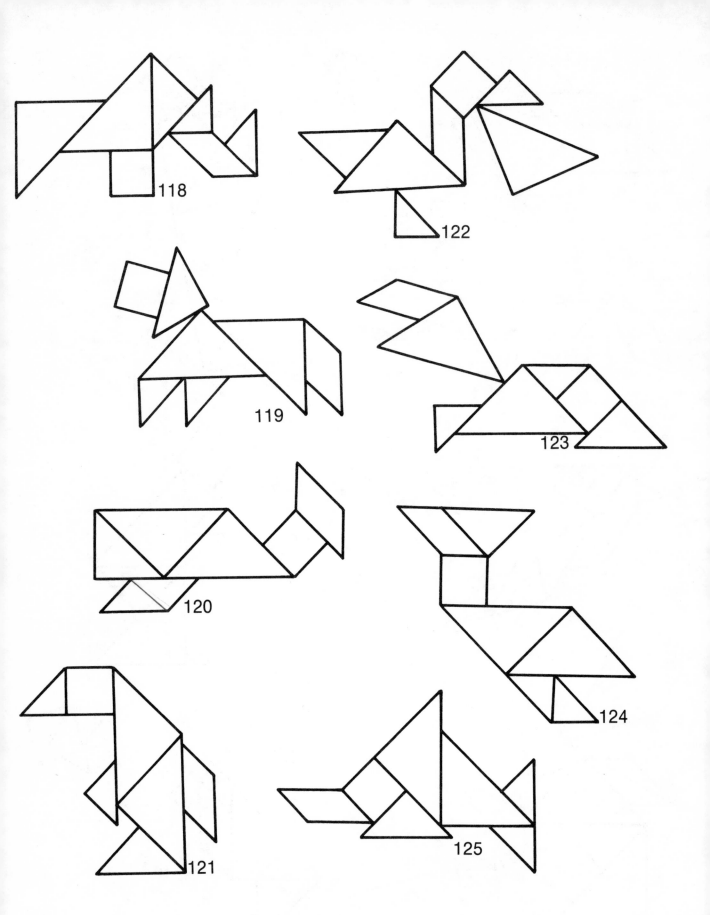

118

122

119

123

120

124

121

125

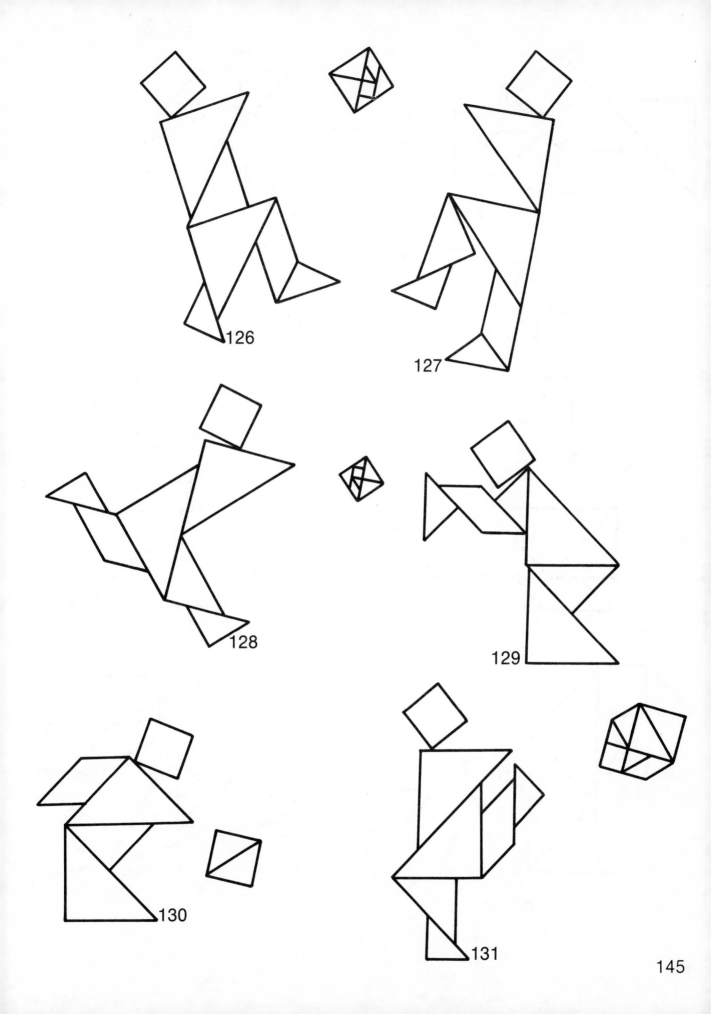

126

127

128

129

130

131

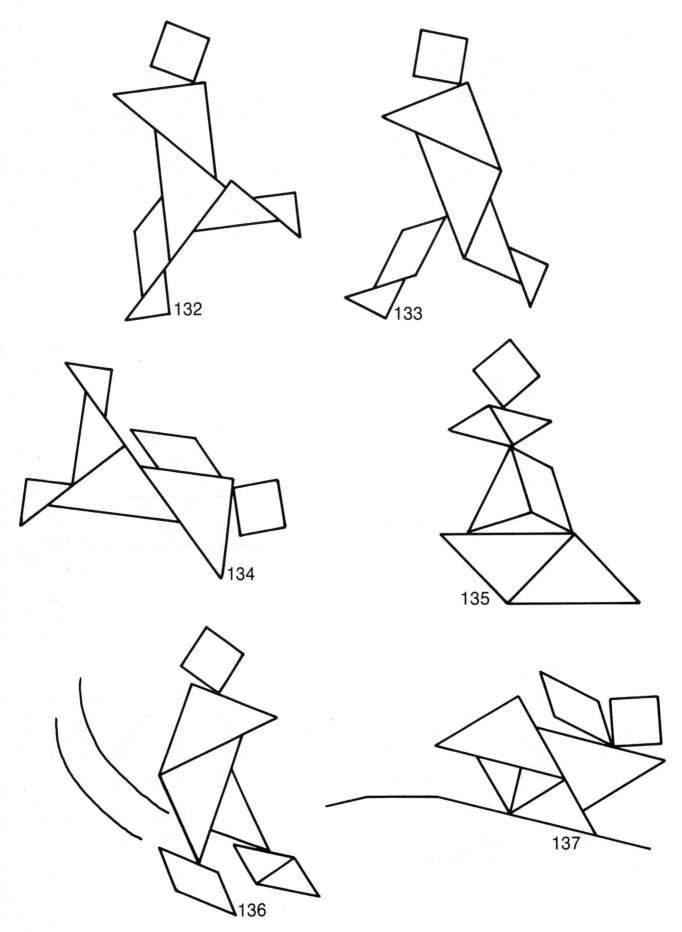

132

133

134

135

136

137

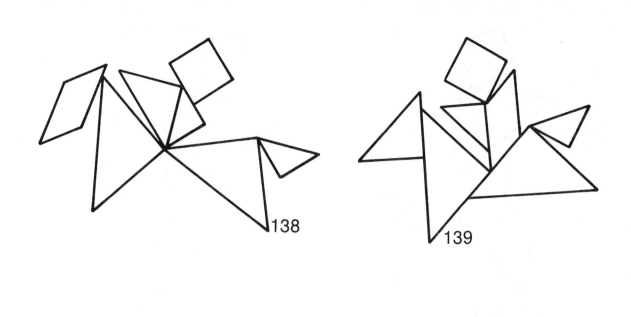

138

139

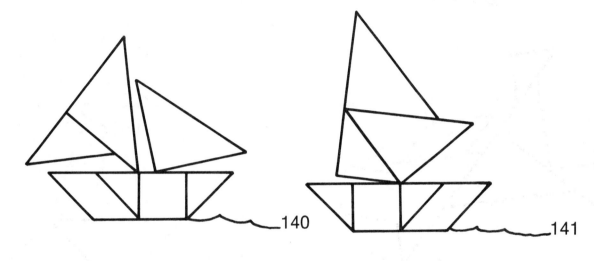

140

141

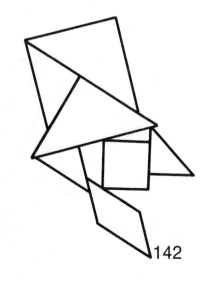

142

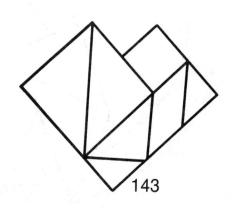

143

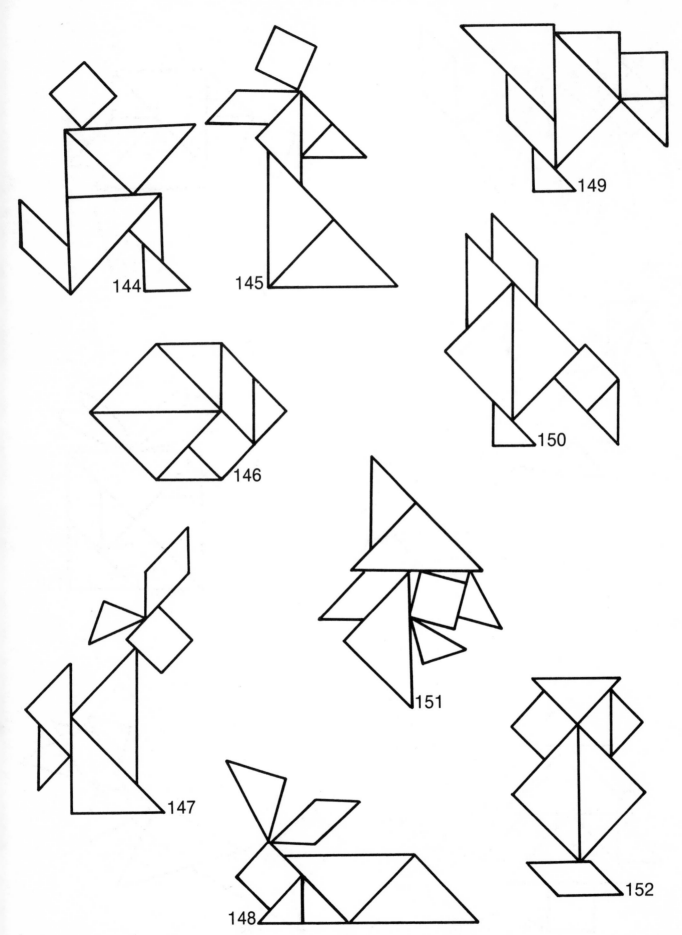

144

145

149

146

150

147

148

151

152

153

157

154

155

158

156

159

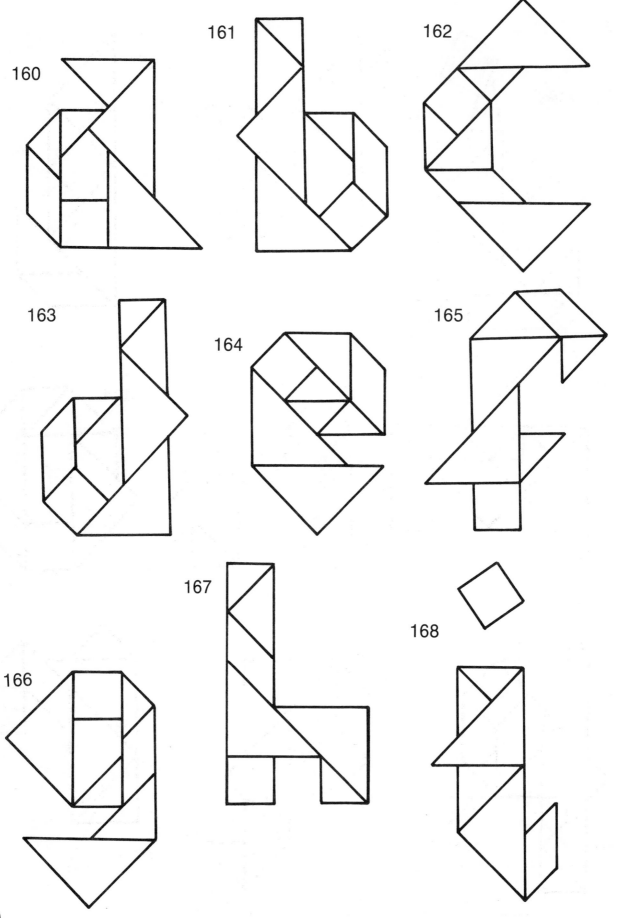

160

161

162

163

164

165

166

167

168

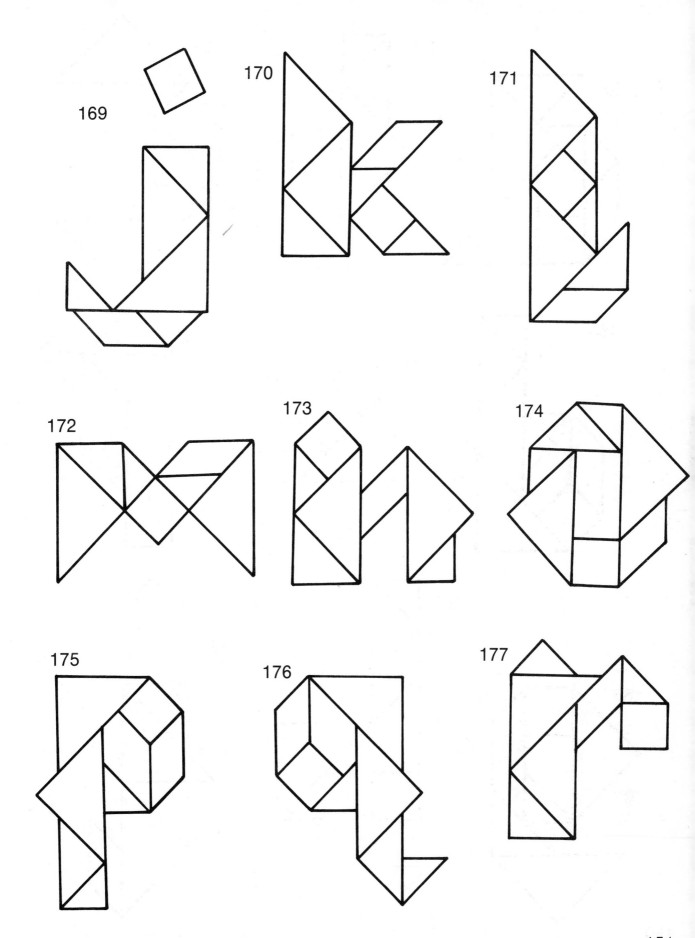

169

170

171

172

173

174

175

176

177

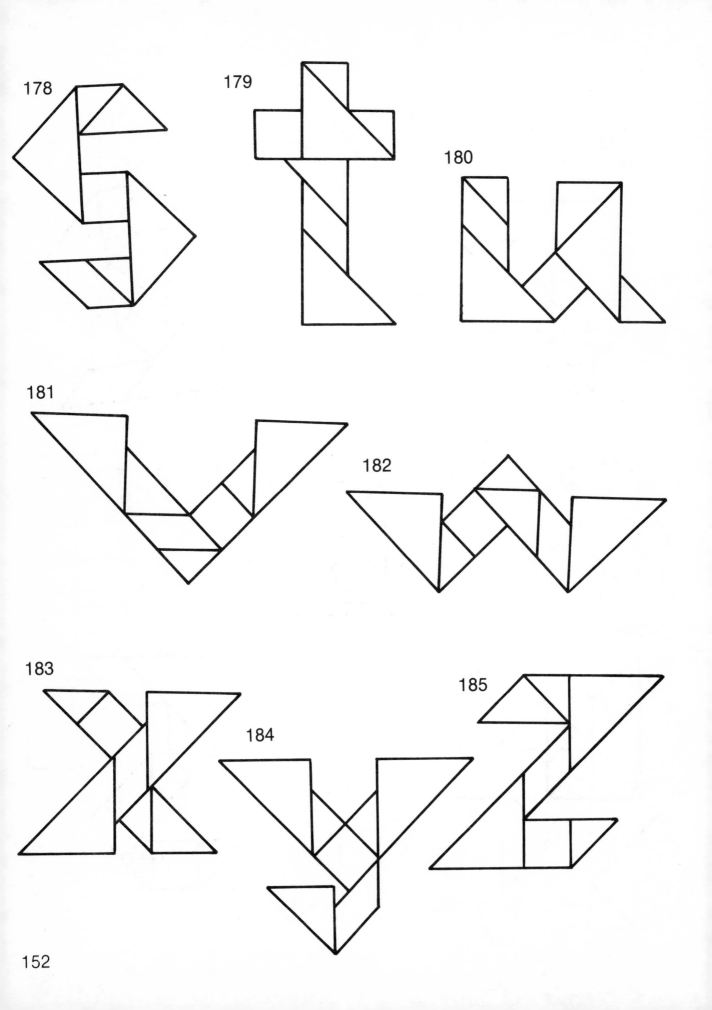

178

179

180

181

182

183

184

185

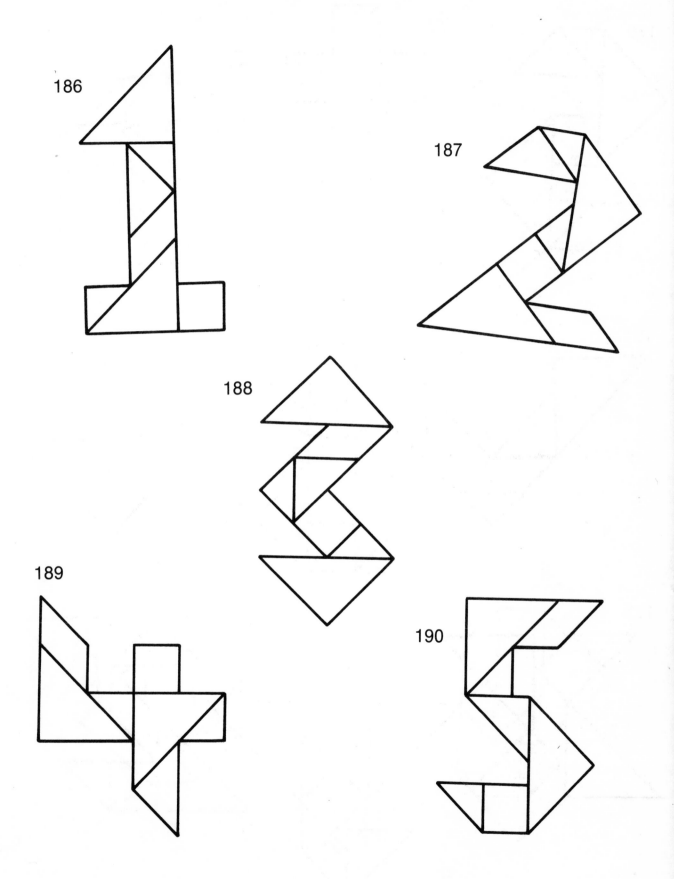

186

187

188

189

190

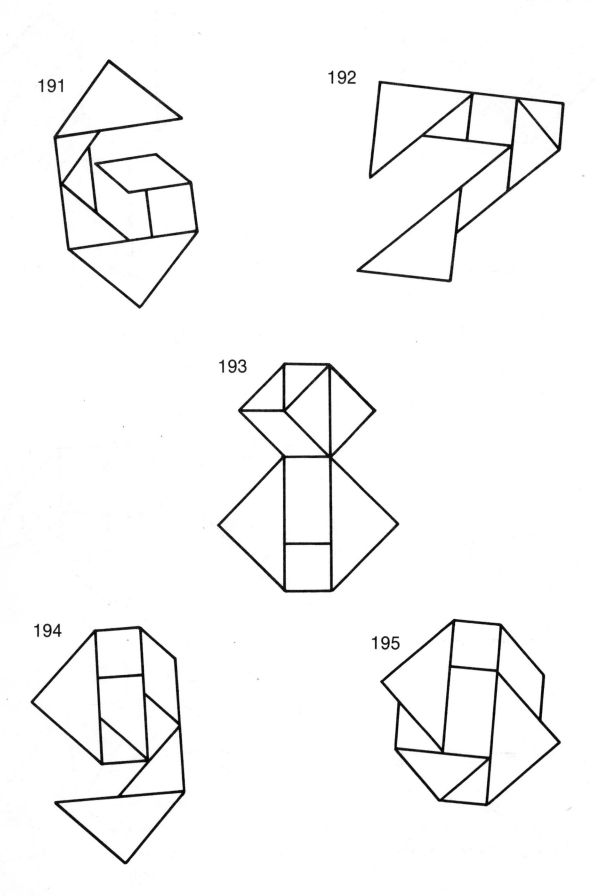

191

192

193

194

195

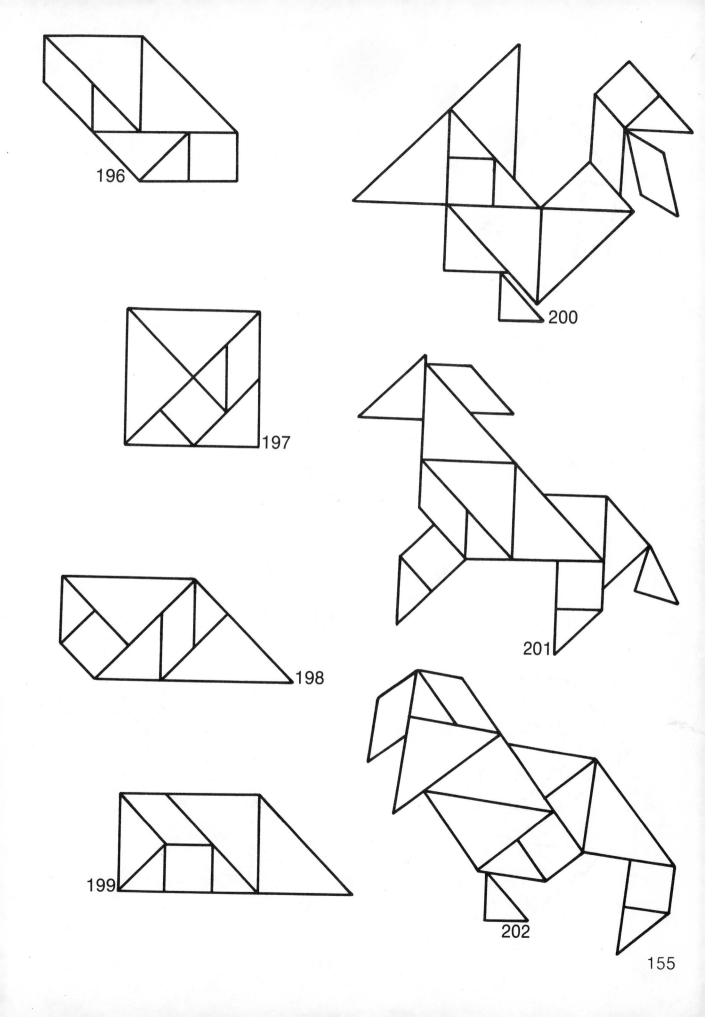

196

197

198

199

200

201

202

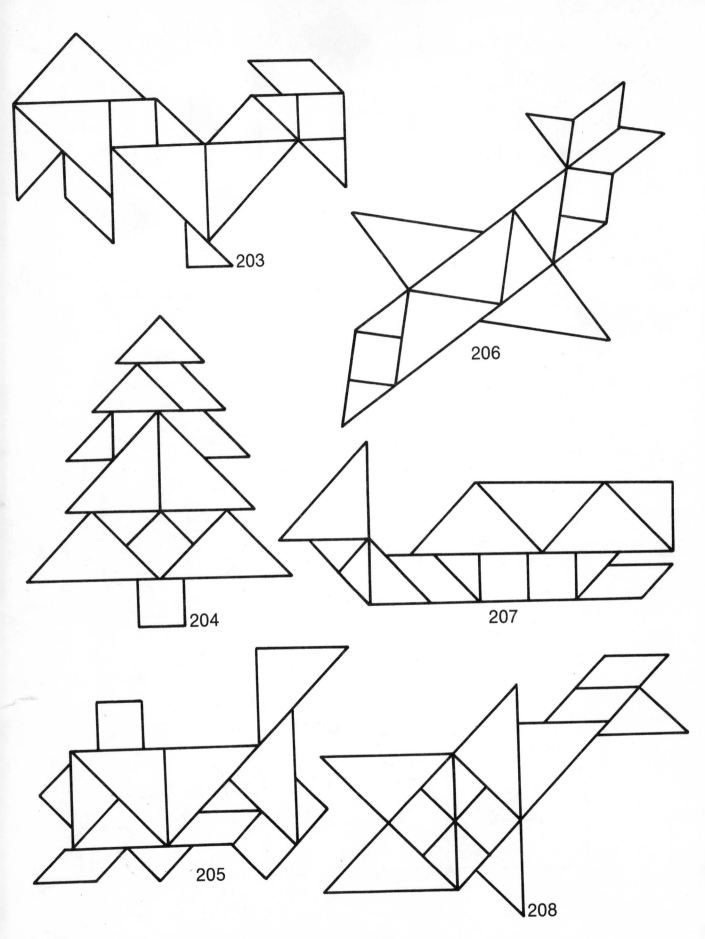

203

206

204

207

205

208

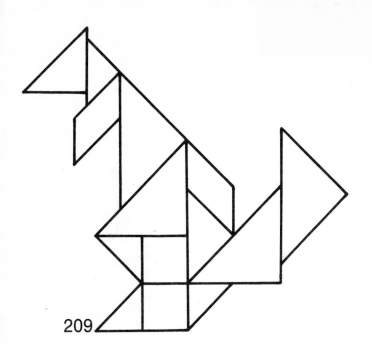

209

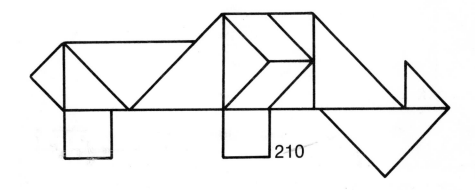

210

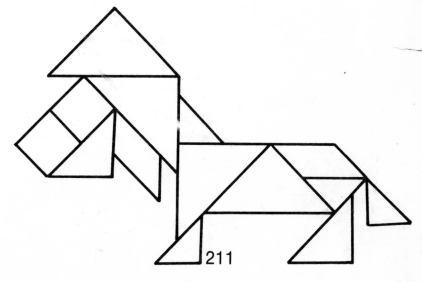

211

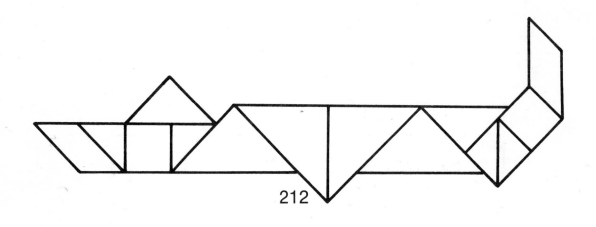

212

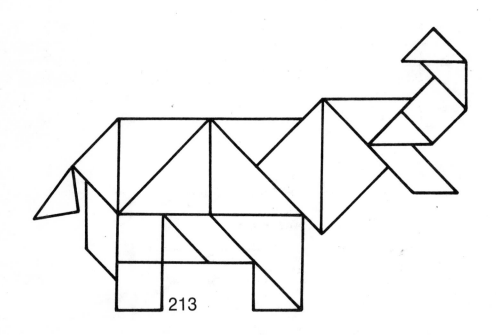

213